SCOTT FORESMAN READING STREET

Weekly Tests
for College and Career Readiness

GRADE 1

S0-AYS-944

Glenview, Illinois

Boston, Massachusetts

Chandler, Arizona

Upper Saddle River, New Jersey

ALWAYS LEARNING

PEARSON

Copyright © Pearson Education, Inc., or its affiliates. All Rights Reserved. Printed in the United States of America. This publication is protected by copyright, and permission should be obtained from the publisher prior to any prohibited reproduction, storage in a retrieval system, or transmission in any form or by any means, electronic, mechanical, photocopying, recording, or likewise. The publisher hereby grants permission to reproduce these pages, in part or in whole, for classroom use only, the number not to exceed the number of students in each class. Notice of copyright must appear on all copies. For information regarding permissions, write to Rights Management & Contracts, Pearson Education, Inc., One Lake Street, Upper Saddle River, New Jersey 07458.

Pearson, Scott Foresman, and Pearson Scott Foresman are trademarks, in the U.S. and/or other countries, of Pearson Education, Inc., or its affiliates.

Common Core State Standards: © Copyright 2010. National Governors Association Center for Best Practices and Council of Chief State School Officers. All rights reserved.

ISBN-13: 978-0-328-79863-6
ISBN-10:   0-328-79863-0
7 8 9 10 V001 17 16 15

Contents

Unit R My World

Unit 1 Animals, Tame and Wild

Unit 2 Communities

Copyright © Pearson Education, Inc., or its affiliates. All Rights Reserved.

Unit 3 Changes

Unit 4 Treasures

Unit 5 Great Ideas

Copyright © Pearson Education, Inc., or its affiliates. All Rights Reserved.

Name _____

**Directions: Read aloud the following passage to children.
Then read aloud each test item.**

A Tidy Room

"Hannah, you must clean your room!" said Mom one Saturday morning. "There's so much stuff piled up that I can hardly see the furniture!"

"I can't do it right now," said Hannah. "I have to find my baseball cap. I need it for the game this afternoon."

"It will be easier to find the cap in a tidy room," said Mom. "I'll help you."

Hannah and her mom started working on the pile of books and toys that covered her dresser. "Look, Mom!" cried Hannah. "I found a box of crayons, and here's a picture I made for you and Dad."

"Thank you, dear. It's lovely," said Mom with a smile. "Aren't you glad we're cleaning your room?"

"Yes! I'm finding a lot of things I've been missing. Look, here's the jump rope I was looking for. It's wrapped around Mr. Bear."

Copyright © Pearson Education, Inc., or its affiliates. All Rights Reserved.

Next

Hannah put her favorite teddy on her bed and then thought to look under the bed, where she found a library book. "I'm so glad I found this," she said. "It's due this week!"

Hannah and Mom worked and worked. Hannah's room looked great, but they still hadn't found her baseball cap. "Are you sure you didn't leave it somewhere else?" asked Mom.

Hannah didn't answer because at that moment Dad came to the room with Ben, Hannah's three-year-old brother. "Your room looks fantastic!" said Dad.

"Thanks, Dad," Hannah replied, but then something caught her eye. She looked closely at her little brother. Ben was wearing her baseball cap! "Look, Mom!" Hannah pointed and laughed. "Now I have my cap and a tidy room too!"

Copyright © Pearson Education, Inc., or its affiliates. All Rights Reserved.

Next

Name _____

Text-Based Comprehension

Directions: Read aloud each question below and have children choose the best answer.

1. Part A

Who is the main character in the story?

 Mom

 Hannah

 Dad

Part B

Which detail from the story helps you know who the main character is?

 "Hannah, you must clean your room!"

 "at that moment Dad came to the room"

 "Ben was wearing her baseball cap!"

Copyright © Pearson Education, Inc., or its affiliates. All Rights Reserved.

COMMON CORE STATE STANDARDS

Literature 1. Ask and answer questions about key details in a text. **Literature 3.** Describe characters, settings, and major events in a story, using key details. **Speaking/Listening 2.** Ask and answer questions about key details in a text read aloud or information presented orally or through other media.

Next

2. Part A

How does Hannah feel as she cleans her room?

 happy

 sad

● tired

Part B

Which detail in the story helps you know how Hannah feels as she cleans her room?

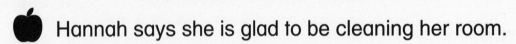 Hannah says she is glad to be cleaning her room.

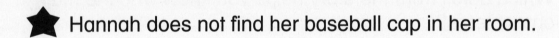 Hannah does not find her baseball cap in her room.

● Hannah finds her jump rope wrapped around Mr. Bear.

Copyright © Pearson Education, Inc., or its affiliates. All Rights Reserved.

COMMON CORE STATE STANDARDS

Literature 1. Ask and answer questions about key details in a text. **Literature 3.** Describe characters, settings, and major events in a story, using key details. **Speaking/Listening 2.** Ask and answer questions about key details in a text read aloud or information presented orally or through other media.

Next

Name _____

Vocabulary

Directions: Read aloud each question below and have children choose the best answer.

3. Part A

Dad says that Hannah's room looks "fantastic." What does the word "fantastic" mean in the story?

🍎 very strange

⭐ very nice

⚫ very fancy

Part B

Which detail from the story helps you understand the meaning of the word "fantastic"?

🍎 "Now I have my cap and a tidy room too!"

⭐ "I'm finding a lot of things"

⚫ "Hannah's room looked great"

Copyright © Pearson Education, Inc., or its affiliates. All Rights Reserved.

COMMON CORE STATE STANDARDS

Language 4. Determine or clarify the meaning of unknown and multiple-meaning words and phrases based on *grade 1 reading and content,* choosing flexibly from an array of strategies. **Language 4.a.** Use sentence-level context as a clue to the meaning of a word or phrase.

Next

4. Part A

Nouns name people, animals, and things.
Which of the following nouns names a person?

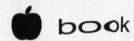 book

⭐ Mr. Bear

⬤ Ben

Part B

Which detail from the story helps you know the noun you chose in Part A is a person?

🍎 Hannah had a name for her favorite teddy.

⭐ Hannah and Mom cleaned the room together.

⬤ Ben is Hannah's three-year-old brother.

Copyright © Pearson Education, Inc., or its affiliates. All Rights Reserved.

COMMON CORE STATE STANDARDS

Language 1.b. Use common, proper, and possessive nouns. **Language 4.a.** Use sentence-level context as a clue to the meaning of a word or phrase. **Language 5.a.** Sort words into categories (e.g., colors, clothing) to gain a sense of the concepts the categories represent.

Next

Name _____

Writing — Constructed Response

Hannah cleaned her room and found some things that were missing. What are two things Hannah found in her room? Where did she find them? Complete the sentences to tell what Hannah found and where she found them. Circle the nouns in your sentences.

Hannah found _____ .

It was _____ .

Hannah found _____ .

It was _____ .

Copyright © Pearson Education, Inc., or its affiliates. All Rights Reserved.

To the Teacher: Use the Writing Rubric on page T19 to assess children's writing.

COMMON CORE STATE STANDARDS

Literature 3. Describe characters, settings, and major events in a story, using key details. **Writing 2.** Write informative/explanatory texts in which they name a topic, supply some facts about the topic, and provide some sense of closure. **Language 1.b.** Use common, proper, and possessive nouns.

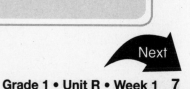
Next

Writing — Extended Response

You have listened to or read two stories about characters in their rooms.

- "A Tidy Room"
- *Sam*

Think about the characters in the two stories. Where are the characters? What things do they have in that place? How are the places alike? How are they different? Use ideas from both stories in your sentences.

To the Teacher: Tell children they may use the space on this page to plan their writing. Then have them write their response on the following pages. Use the Writing Rubric on page T20 to assess children's writing.

COMMON CORE STATE STANDARDS

Literature 3. Describe characters, settings, and major events in a story, using key details. **Writing 2.** Write informative/explanatory texts in which they name a topic, supply some facts about the topic, and provide some sense of closure.

Copyright © Pearson Education, Inc., or its affiliates. All Rights Reserved.

Next

Name _____

_____
- - - - - - - - - - - - - - - - - -
_____

_____
- - - - - - - - - - - - - - - - - -
_____

_____
- - - - - - - - - - - - - - - - - -
_____

_____
- - - - - - - - - - - - - - - - - -
_____

_____
- - - - - - - - - - - - - - - - - -
_____

_____
- - - - - - - - - - - - - - - - - -
_____

_____
- - - - - - - - - - - - - - - - - -
_____

_____
- - - - - - - - - - - - - - - - - -
_____

Copyright © Pearson Education, Inc., or its affiliates. All Rights Reserved.

Next

Copyright © Pearson Education, Inc., or its affiliates. All Rights Reserved.

Name _____

**Directions: Read aloud the following passage to children.
Then read aloud each test item.**

Surprise!

The James family was busy at work in their kitchen. Although they didn't have a big house, the kitchen was quite large, and it was usually the center of family activity. Today, Mom and the kids were preparing a special surprise birthday dinner for Aunt Sue. Jacob was setting the table with his younger sister, Carla. Their older sister, Emily, was tossing the salad.

Earlier in the day, the kids had . . . put up signs and decorations they had made. The kitchen looked beautiful! The only family member that hadn't helped out was Buddy, their dog. Poor Buddy! There wasn't much he could do, although he wanted so much to be a part of things.

Soon it was almost time for Aunt Sue to arrive. Mom was still busy cooking, so she put Jacob and Emily in charge of wrapping Aunt Sue's gifts. They let Carla put the bows on top.

Copyright © Pearson Education, Inc., or its affiliates. All Rights Reserved.

Next

When Mom looked out the kitchen window again, she saw Aunt Sue walking toward the front door with Grandma and Grandpa. "Oh my goodness!" she said. "We're not quite ready — we need a little more time!"

"I know what to do," said Emily. "I'll ask her to take Buddy for a walk. That should give us the time we need."

"That's perfect, dear," said Mom. So as soon as Aunt Sue came in the front door, Emily gave her Buddy's leash, and the three of them left.

A little later, when they returned, everything was ready. "Surprise! Surprise!" yelled the group, as they led Aunt Sue into the kitchen. . . .

Copyright © Pearson Education, Inc., or its affiliates. All Rights Reserved.

Next

Name _____

Text-Based Comprehension

Directions: Read aloud each question below and have children choose the best answer.

I. **Part A**

Where does the story take place?

🍎 the family's kitchen

⭐ the living room

⬤ the city park

Part B

Which detail from the story helps you identify the setting?

🍎 she saw Aunt Sue walking toward the front door

⭐ The James family was busy at work in their kitchen.

⬤ Emily gave her Buddy's leash, and the three of them left.

Copyright © Pearson Education, Inc., or its affiliates. All Rights Reserved.

COMMON CORE STATE STANDARDS

Literature 1. Ask and answer questions about key details in a text. **Literature 3.** Describe characters, settings, and major events in a story, using key details. **Speaking/Listening 2.** Ask and answer questions about key details in a text read aloud or information presented orally or through other media.

Next

2. Part A

How did the children change the way the setting looked?

🍎 They decorated it.

⭐ They painted it.

⚫ They cleaned it.

Part B

Which detail from the story helps you know how the children changed the way the setting looked?

🍎 the kids had . . . put up signs and decorations they had made

⭐ Their older sister, Emily, was tossing the salad.

⚫ A little later, when they returned, everything was ready.

Copyright © Pearson Education, Inc., or its affiliates. All Rights Reserved.

COMMON CORE STATE STANDARDS

Literature 1. Ask and answer questions about key details in a text. **Literature 3.** Describe characters, settings, and major events in a story, using key details. **Speaking/Listening 2.** Ask and answer questions about key details in a text read aloud or information presented orally or through other media.

Next

Name _____

Vocabulary

Directions: Read aloud each question below and have children choose the best answer.

3. Part A

What describing word could you use to tell about the size of the kitchen?

 big

 pretty

 tiny

Part B

Which detail from the story helps you know which describing word can be used to tell about the size of the kitchen?

 it was usually the center of family activity

 the kitchen was quite large

 The kitchen looked beautiful!

Copyright © Pearson Education, Inc., or its affiliates. All Rights Reserved.

COMMON CORE STATE STANDARDS

Language 1.f. Use frequently occurring adjectives. **Language 4.** Determine or clarify the meaning of unknown and multiple-meaning words and phrases based on *grade 1 reading and content,* choosing flexibly from an array of strategies. **Language 4.a.** Use sentence-level context as a clue to the meaning of a word or phrase.

Next

4. Part A

The story uses the words "Poor Buddy" to tell about the family dog. What does the describing word "poor" mean in the story?

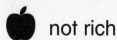 not rich

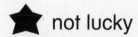 not lucky

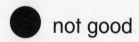 not good

Part B

Which detail from the story helps you understand the meaning of the word "poor"?

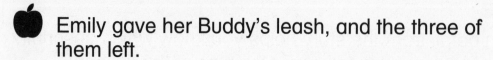 Emily gave her Buddy's leash, and the three of them left.

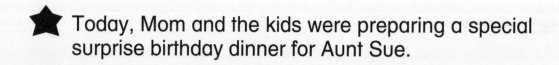 Today, Mom and the kids were preparing a special surprise birthday dinner for Aunt Sue.

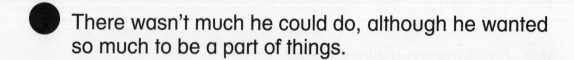 There wasn't much he could do, although he wanted so much to be a part of things.

Copyright © Pearson Education, Inc., or its affiliates. All Rights Reserved.

COMMON CORE STATE STANDARDS

Language 1.f. Use frequently occurring adjectives. **Language 4.** Determine or clarify the meaning of unknown and multiple-meaning words and phrases based on *grade 1 reading and content,* choosing flexibly from an array of strategies. **Language 4.a.** Use sentence-level context as a clue to the meaning of a word or phrase. **Language 5.** With guidance and support from adults, demonstrate understanding of word relationships and nuances in word meanings.

Next

Name _____

Writing – Constructed Response

The children put up signs for the surprise party. What do you think the signs said? Draw your sign. Write a sentence that could be used on the sign. Use nouns from the story in your sentence.

Copyright © Pearson Education, Inc., or its affiliates. All Rights Reserved.

To the Teacher: Use the Writing Rubric on page T19 to assess children's writing.

COMMON CORE STATE STANDARDS

Literature 1. Ask and answer questions about key details in a text. **Writing 2.** Write informative/explanatory texts in which they name a topic, supply some facts about the topic, and provide some sense of closure. **Language 1.b.** Use common, proper, and possessive nouns.

Next

Writing — Extended Response

You have listened to or read two stories about families.

- "Surprise!"
- *Snap!*

Think about the settings of the stories. Write to tell how the settings are alike and how they are different.

Copyright © Pearson Education, Inc., or its affiliates. All Rights Reserved.

To the Teacher: Tell children they may use the space on this page to plan their writing. Then have them write their response on the following pages. Use the Writing Rubric on page T20 to assess children's writing.

COMMON CORE STATE STANDARDS

Literature 1. Ask and answer questions about key details in a text. **Writing 2.** Write informative/explanatory texts in which they name a topic, supply some facts about the topic, and provide some sense of closure. **Language 1.b.** Use common, proper, and possessive nouns.

Next

Name _____

_____

_____

_____

_____

_____

_____

_____

_____

_____

_____

_____

_____

_____

Copyright © Pearson Education, Inc., or its affiliates. All Rights Reserved.

Next

Copyright © Pearson Education, Inc., or its affiliates. All Rights Reserved.

Name _____

**Directions: Read aloud the following passage to children.
Then read aloud each test item.**

A City Garden

One morning as Danny waited for the school bus . . . , he noticed that the small building across the street was being torn down. The building was old and had been empty for a long time. Danny wondered what might be built in its place. He waited several weeks, but . . . the lot remained empty. One day . . . , he had an idea.

. . . Danny talked to his father about his idea. "Wouldn't it be nice to have a garden in that empty lot across the street?" he asked. . . .

"Yes, that is a great idea!" said his dad. "I will talk to some of our neighbors, and we'll see if it's possible." So Mr. Torres and several neighbors went to the mayor's office, and . . . they got permission to create a city garden!

. . . Each weekend, Danny, his dad, and all their friends and neighbors worked together, planting, watering, and weeding. Soon, the empty lot became a lovely garden filled with flowers and vegetables.

Copyright © Pearson Education, Inc., or its affiliates. All Rights Reserved.

Next

. . . People picked the vegetables that were ripe and sold them. They used the money to create a sitting area with a lawn and benches. . . .

The city garden became famous. One day, a reporter came by to interview Mr. Torres and some of the other people working in the garden. "The people in the neighborhood have created something very special," said the reporter. . . . "Who came up with this terrific idea? Was it you?"

"No, it wasn't me," said Mr. Torres. "It was my son Danny's idea, and I'm very proud of him."

Copyright © Pearson Education, Inc., or its affiliates. All Rights Reserved.

Next

Name _____

Text-Based Comprehension

Directions: Read aloud each question below and have children choose the best answer.

I. Part A

What happens at the beginning of the story?

🍎 Mr. Torres goes to the mayor's office.

⭐ Danny sees a building being torn down.

⬤ People throw trash in the empty lot.

Part B

Which detail from the story helps you know what happens at the beginning of the story?

🍎 People picked the vegetables that were ripe and sold them.

⭐ the small building across the street was being torn down

⬤ So Mr. Torres and several neighbors went to the mayor's office

Copyright © Pearson Education, Inc., or its affiliates. All Rights Reserved.

COMMON CORE STATE STANDARDS

Literature 1. Ask and answer questions about key details in a text. **Literature 3.** Describe characters, settings, and major events in a story, using key details. **Speaking/Listening 2.** Ask and answer questions about key details in a text read aloud or information presented orally or through other media.

Next

2. Part A

The empty lot is not pretty. How do the neighbors solve this problem?

🍎 They put up a building.

⭐ They sell the land.

⬤ They plant a garden.

Part B

Which detail from the story helps you know how the neighbors solve the problem?

🍎 Soon, the empty lot became a lovely garden

⭐ the lot remained empty

⬤ the small building across the street was being torn down

Copyright © Pearson Education, Inc., or its affiliates. All Rights Reserved.

COMMON CORE STATE STANDARDS

Literature 1. Ask and answer questions about key details in a text. **Literature 3.** Describe characters, settings, and major events in a story, using key details. **Speaking/Listening 2.** Ask and answer questions about key details in a text read aloud or information presented orally or through other media.

Next

Name _____

Vocabulary

Directions: Read aloud each question below and have children choose the best answer.

3. **Part A**

   The story says that Mr. Torres and the neighbors got permission to create a garden. What do the words "got permission" mean in the story?

   🍎 would not be allowed

   ⭐ were given approval

   ⬤ had to promise

   Part B

   Which detail from the story helps you know what the words "got permission" mean?

   🍎 Soon, the empty lot became a lovely garden

   ⭐ "…he noticed that the small building across the street was being torn down."

   ⬤ Danny talked to his father about his idea.

COMMON CORE STATE STANDARDS

Language 4. Determine or clarify the meaning of unknown and multiple-meaning words and phrases based on *grade 1 reading and content,* choosing flexibly from an array of strategies. **Language 4.a.** Use sentence-level context as a clue to the meaning of a word or phrase.

Copyright © Pearson Education, Inc., or its affiliates. All Rights Reserved.

Next

4. Part A

"They used the money to create a sitting area with a lawn and benches." What does the word "benches" mean in the story?

 green grass

 tables for tools

 long seats

Part B

Which detail from the following sentence helps you know what the word "benches" means?
"They used the money to create a sitting area with a lawn and benches."

 the money

 a sitting area

 a lawn

Copyright © Pearson Education, Inc., or its affiliates. All Rights Reserved.

COMMON CORE STATE STANDARDS

Language 4. Determine or clarify the meaning of unknown and multiple-meaning words and phrases based on *grade 1 reading and content*, choosing flexibly from an array of strategies. **Language 4.a.** Use sentence-level context as a clue to the meaning of a word or phrase.

Next

Name _____

Writing — Constructed Response

Mr. Torres and some neighbors went to the mayor's office and got permission to plant a garden. What did they say to the mayor to get permission? Complete these sentences. Write what you think Mr. Torres said to the mayor. Give reasons why the mayor should approve a garden.

The lot is _____.

A garden would _____.

Many neighbors will _____.

To the Teacher: Use the Writing Rubric on page T19 to assess children's writing.

COMMON CORE STATE STANDARDS

Literature 1. Ask and answer questions about key details in a text. **Literature 3.** Describe characters, settings, and major events in a story, using key details. **Writing 2.** Write informative/explanatory texts in which they name a topic, supply some facts about the topic, and provide some sense of closure.

Copyright © Pearson Education, Inc., or its affiliates. All Rights Reserved.

Next

Writing — Extended Response

You have listened to or read two stories about outdoor activities.

- "A City Garden"
- *Tip and Tam*

What do the characters in each story do outdoors? Write sentences telling how the characters in both stories enjoy the outdoors. Tell how the outdoor activities of the characters in "A City Garden" are different from the outdoor activities of the characters in *Tip and Tam.*

To the Teacher: Tell children they may use the space on this page to plan their writing. Then have them write their response on the following pages. Use the Writing Rubric on page T20 to assess children's writing.

Copyright © Pearson Education, Inc., or its affiliates. All Rights Reserved.

COMMON CORE STATE STANDARDS

Literature 1. Ask and answer questions about key details in a text. **Literature 3.** Describe characters, settings, and major events in a story, using key details. **Literature 9.** Compare and contrast the adventures and experiences of characters in stories. **Writing 2.** Write informative/explanatory texts in which they name a topic, supply some facts about the topic, and provide some sense of closure.

Next

Name _____

Copyright © Pearson Education, Inc., or its affiliates. All Rights Reserved.

Next

Copyright © Pearson Education, Inc., or its affiliates. All Rights Reserved.

Name _____

**Directions: Read aloud the following passage to children.
Then read aloud each test item.**

A Neighborhood Picnic

Patty Pig and her next-door neighbor, Jenny Hen, read the sign on the tree: "Come to a neighborhood picnic on Saturday at Duck Lake. Bring good food to share with your neighbors. There will be games and races."

"I'm going to bring a big fruit salad," said Jenny Hen, fluttering her feathers. . . .

"I'm going to bring lots of tasty sandwiches," said Patty Pig. . . .

However, when Saturday came, it was raining so hard that a picnic at Duck Lake was impossible. Patty . . . had a brilliant idea. She called Jenny to tell her. "I know how we can still have our picnic!" said Patty excitedly.

"How?" asked Jenny Hen. "It's pouring outside!"

"We can have an indoor picnic in our home—yours and mine!" said Patty. "We'll move our furniture against the walls and make a covered passage between your house and mine so people can walk back and forth."

"You're a genius!" said Jenny. "Let's call our neighbors and spread the news."

Copyright © Pearson Education, Inc., or its affiliates. All Rights Reserved.

Next

By noon, their furniture was pushed against the walls. Then Patty and Jenny made a covered path between their homes by tying umbrellas together. Soon the neighbors began to arrive with their food and blankets.

Since there were a few animals that were new to the neighborhood, Patty wanted to welcome them. "I'd like to introduce myself," she said. "My name is Patty and that is my dear friend, Jenny, on the porch next door. Welcome to our first neighborhood indoor picnic!"

The picnic turned out to be a huge success. Although there were no races, the animals sang songs, told amusing jokes, and shared stories. In fact, everyone had such a wonderful time that they decided to have other indoor picnics during rainy or cold weather!

Copyright © Pearson Education, Inc., or its affiliates. All Rights Reserved.

Next

Name _____

Text-Based Comprehension

Directions: Read aloud each question below and have children choose the best answer.

1. Part A

What makes the story "A Neighborhood Picnic" a fantasy?

🍎 The characters are animals that act like people.

⭐ A pig and a hen are two of the characters in the story.

⬤ A sign for a neighborhood picnic has been posted on a tree.

Part B

Which detail from the story helps you know the story is a fantasy?

🍎 "Welcome to our first neighborhood indoor picnic!"

⭐ "Bring good food to share with your neighbors. There will be games and races."

⬤ "I'm going to bring a big fruit salad," said Jenny Hen, fluttering her feathers.

Copyright © Pearson Education, Inc., or its affiliates. All Rights Reserved.

COMMON CORE STATE STANDARDS

Literature 1. Ask and answer questions about key details in a text. **Literature 3.** Describe characters, settings, and major events in a story, using key details. **Speaking/Listening 2.** Ask and answer questions about key details in a text read aloud or information presented orally or through other media.

Next

2. Part A

What problem do the characters have?

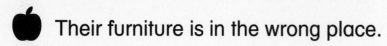 Their furniture is in the wrong place.

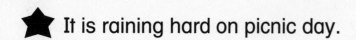 It is raining hard on picnic day.

● There is not enough food for everyone.

Part B

Which detail from the story helps you know what problem the characters have?

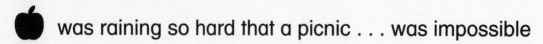 was raining so hard that a picnic . . . was impossible

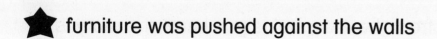 furniture was pushed against the walls

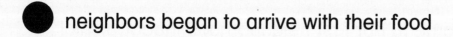 neighbors began to arrive with their food

Copyright © Pearson Education, Inc., or its affiliates. All Rights Reserved.

COMMON CORE STATE STANDARDS

Literature 1. Ask and answer questions about key details in a text. **Literature 3.** Describe characters, settings, and major events in a story, using key details. **Speaking/Listening 2.** Ask and answer questions about key details in a text read aloud or information presented orally or through other media.

Next

Name _____

Vocabulary

Directions: Read aloud each question below and have children choose the best answer.

3. Part A

"Let's call our neighbors and spread the news." What does the word "spread" mean in the story?

 send out

 hide

 unfold

Part B

Which detail from the following sentence helps you know what the word "spread" means?
"Let's call our neighbors and spread the news."

 the news

 our neighbors

 Let's call

Copyright © Pearson Education, Inc., or its affiliates. All Rights Reserved.

COMMON CORE STATE STANDARDS

Language 4. Determine or clarify the meaning of unknown and multiple-meaning words and phrases based on *grade 1 reading and content*, choosing flexibly from an array of strategies. **Language 4.a.** Use sentence-level context as a clue to the meaning of a word or phrase.

Next

4. Part A

At the picnic, Patty says "I'd like to introduce myself." What does the word "introduce" mean in the story?

🍎 begin something such as a speech

⭐ tell one's name to someone

● start the use of something

Part B

Which story detail helps you understand the meaning of "introduce" in the story?

🍎 the neighbors began to arrive

⭐ Patty wanted to welcome them.

● "My name is Patty"

Copyright © Pearson Education, Inc., or its affiliates. All Rights Reserved.

COMMON CORE STATE STANDARDS

Language 4. Determine or clarify the meaning of unknown and multiple-meaning words and phrases based on *grade 1 reading and content,* choosing flexibly from an array of strategies. **Language 4.a.** Use sentence-level context as a clue to the meaning of a word or phrase.

Next

Name _____

Writing — Constructed Response

In the story "A Neighborhood Picnic," Jenny calls Patty a genius. Write sentences that tell why Jenny thinks Patty is a "genius." Use information from the story in your sentences.

_____

_____

_____

_____

_____

_____

_____

_____

_____

_____

Copyright © Pearson Education, Inc., or its affiliates. All Rights Reserved.

To the Teacher: Use the Writing Rubric on page T19 to assess children's writing.

COMMON CORE STATE STANDARDS

Literature 1. Ask and answer questions about key details in a text. **Literature 3.** Describe characters, settings, and major events in a story, using key details. **Writing 2.** Write informative/explanatory texts in which they name a topic, supply some facts about the topic, and provide some sense of closure.

Next

Writing — Extended Response

You have listened to or read two stories about neighborhood friends.

- "A Neighborhood Picnic"
- *The Big Top*

Both "A Neighborhood Picnic" and *The Big Top* are fictional stories. "A Neighborhood Picnic" is a fantasy. *The Big Top* is realistic fiction. Write sentences that tell what makes the stories different kinds of fiction. Use the story titles in your sentences.

Copyright © Pearson Education, Inc., or its affiliates. All Rights Reserved.

To the Teacher: Tell children they may use the space on this page to plan their writing. Then have them write their response on the following pages. Use the Writing Rubric on page T20 to assess children's writing.

COMMON CORE STATE STANDARDS

Literature 1. Ask and answer questions about key details in a text. **Literature 3.** Describe characters, settings, and major events in a story, using key details. **Literature 9.** Compare and contrast the adventures and experiences of characters in stories. **Writing 2.** Write informative/explanatory texts in which they name a topic, supply some facts about the topic, and provide some sense of closure.

Next

Name _____

Copyright © Pearson Education, Inc., or its affiliates. All Rights Reserved.

Next

Copyright © Pearson Education, Inc., or its affiliates. All Rights Reserved.

Name _____

Directions: Read aloud the following passage to children.
Then read aloud each test item.

Early for School

Jason liked school a lot, but he was often late. Today he had spent too much time daydreaming over breakfast until Mom told him what time it was. Luckily, Jason lived only a block from school. He ran down the block, walked quickly through the large school doors, and hurried down the long hall to his classroom. He tiptoed quietly in and took his seat.

"Good morning, Jason," said his teacher, Miss Parsons. "I was just introducing our new student, Peter Rogers, to the class. Peter and his family moved here from another state, and as it turns out, he lives on your block. So perhaps after school, you and Peter can walk home together."

"Sure, Miss Parsons," said Jason. "It's nice to meet you, Peter." Jason was a very polite boy.

Peter smiled and said thanks, and then the class took out their reading books and started working.

Copyright © Pearson Education, Inc., or its affiliates. All Rights Reserved.

Next

During the day, Jason showed Peter where to find things. He showed his new classmate the library area. He showed him where the pencils and crayons were kept and the chart that listed the class jobs. After lunch, they played ball on the playground.

At the end of the day, Jason and Peter walked home together. They had a lot to talk about. Jason liked his new friend and Peter felt the same way. The boys reached Jason's house first, but before they said good-bye, they made a plan to meet the next morning to walk to school together.

"I'll ring your doorbell early tomorrow, so we can take our time," said Peter.

"That sounds great!" said Jason. "I'll be ready." And he was!

Copyright © Pearson Education, Inc., or its affiliates. All Rights Reserved.

Name _____

Text-Based Comprehension

Directions: Read aloud each question below and have children choose the best answer.

1. Part A

What problem does Jason have?

🍎 Jason lives far from school.

⭐ Jason gets to school late.

⬤ Jason had no friends at school.

Part B

Which detail from the story helps you know what problem Jason has?

🍎 Jason liked school a lot, but he was often late.

⭐ the class took out their reading books and started working

⬤ Jason liked his new friend and Peter felt the same way.

COMMON CORE STATE STANDARDS

Literature 1. Ask and answer questions about key details in a text. **Literature 3.** Describe characters, settings, and major events in a story, using key details. **Speaking/Listening 2.** Ask and answer questions about key details in a text read aloud or information presented orally or through other media.

Copyright © Pearson Education, Inc., or its affiliates. All Rights Reserved.

Next

2. Part A

Who helped Jason solve his problem?

 Mom

 Miss Parsons

 Peter

Part B

Which detail from the story helps you know who helped Jason solve his problem?

 "So perhaps after school, you and Peter can walk home together."

 "I was just introducing our new student, Peter Rogers, to the class."

 "I'll ring your doorbell early tomorrow, so we can take our time," said Peter.

Copyright © Pearson Education, Inc., or its affiliates. All Rights Reserved.

COMMON CORE STATE STANDARDS

Literature 1. Ask and answer questions about key details in a text. **Literature 3.** Describe characters, settings, and major events in a story, using key details. **Speaking/Listening 2.** Ask and answer questions about key details in a text read aloud or information presented orally or through other media.

Next

Name _____

Vocabulary

Directions: Read aloud each question below and have children choose the best answer.

3. Part A

"Peter and his family moved here from another state, and as it turns out, he lives on your block." What does the word "state" mean in that sentence?

🍎 say aloud

⭐ a part of a country

⬤ the condition of something

Part B

Reread this sentence: "Peter and his family moved here from another state, and as it turns out, he lives on your block." Which detail from the sentence helps you know what the word "state" means?

🍎 on your block

⭐ moved here from

⬤ Peter and his family

Copyright © Pearson Education, Inc., or its affiliates. All Rights Reserved.

COMMON CORE STATE STANDARDS

Language 4. Determine or clarify the meaning of unknown and multiple-meaning words and phrases based on *grade 1 reading and content,* choosing flexibly from an array of strategies. **Language 4.a.** Use sentence-level context as a clue to the meaning of a word or phrase.

Next

4. Part A

A describing word tells more about people, places, animals, and things. Which describing word tells more about a person in the story?

🍎 large

⭐ long

⚫ polite

Part B

Which detail from the story helps you know which describing word tells more about the person?

🍎 hurried down the long hall

⭐ showed Peter where to find things

⚫ was a very polite boy

Copyright © Pearson Education, Inc., or its affiliates. All Rights Reserved.

COMMON CORE STATE STANDARDS

Language 1.f. Use frequently occurring adjectives. **Language 4.** Determine or clarify the meaning of unknown and multiple-meaning words and phrases based on *grade 1 reading and content,* choosing flexibly from an array of strategies. **Language 4.a.** Use sentence-level context as a clue to the meaning of a word or phrase.

Next

Name _____

Writing — Constructed Response

In the story "Early for School," Jason and Peter walk home from school together. Which boy lives closer to school? Write sentences telling who lives closer to school and how you know. Use information from the story in your sentences.

_____

- -

_____

- -

_____

- -

_____

- -

_____

- -

_____

- -

_____

- -

_____

- -

To the Teacher: Use the Writing Rubric on page T19 to assess children's writing.

Copyright © Pearson Education, Inc., or its affiliates. All Rights Reserved.

COMMON CORE STATE STANDARDS

Literature 1. Ask and answer questions about key details in a text. **Literature 3.** Describe characters, settings, and major events in a story, using key details. **Writing 2.** Write informative/explanatory texts in which they name a topic, supply some facts about the topic, and provide some sense of closure.

Next

Writing — Extended Response

You have listened to or read two stories about school.

- "Early for School"
- *School Day*

Both "Early for School" and *School Day* are fictional stories. Are they realistic fiction or fantasy? Write sentences that explain what kind of story each one is. Also explain how you know what kind of story each one is. Use the story titles and information from the stories in your sentences.

Copyright © Pearson Education, Inc., or its affiliates. All Rights Reserved.

To the Teacher: Tell children they may use the space on this page to plan their writing. Then have them write their response on the following pages. Use the Writing Rubric on page T20 to assess children's writing.

COMMON CORE STATE STANDARDS

Literature 1. Ask and answer questions about key details in a text. **Literature 3.** Describe characters, settings, and major events in a story, using key details. **Writing 2.** Write informative/explanatory texts in which they name a topic, supply some facts about the topic, and provide some sense of closure.

Next

Name _____

Copyright © Pearson Education, Inc., or its affiliates. All Rights Reserved.

Next

Copyright © Pearson Education, Inc., or its affiliates. All Rights Reserved.

Name _____

Directions: Read aloud the following passage to children.
Then read aloud each test item.

A Busy Day

Bonnie Bear and Betty Bear were neighbors and good friends. Today they sat down to make a list of errands they both needed to do. They had to go to the library . . . and their favorite hat shop.

Their first stop was the library. Bonnie liked books about the . . . planets. So she wanted to browse and look for those kinds of books. Betty liked to read stories about people. . . . When they found books they liked, they checked them out.

"Isn't it curious that we are such good friends, yet we like different kinds of books?" asked Betty. . . .

"Yes, I suppose it is," answered Bonnie. . . .

Then the bears went to their favorite hat shop. Betty tried on a white hat with red polka dots. "I love the color white and I love polka dots!" she said. "This is the hat for me. . . ."

Bonnie tried on a pale blue hat. . . . "Blue is my favorite color," she said. "This is the hat I will buy."

Copyright © Pearson Education, Inc., or its affiliates. All Rights Reserved.

Next

"Isn't it curious that we are such good friends, yet we like different kinds of hats?" asked Betty. . . .

"Yes, I suppose it is," said Bonnie.

Since the bears were done with their errands, they sat down in the park. . . . "I've been thinking about your questions," said Bonnie. "We may not like the same books . . . or hats, but we really like each other, and that's why we're such good friends!" And Betty, of course, agreed.

Copyright © Pearson Education, Inc., or its affiliates. All Rights Reserved.

Next

Name _____

Text-Based Comprehension

Directions: Read aloud each question below and have children choose the best answer.

1. **Part A**

What makes the story "A Busy Day" a fantasy?

🍎 The story events could really happen.

⭐ The main characters in the story are friends.

⬤ The animals in the story act like people.

Part B

Which detail from the story helps you know the story is a fantasy?

🍎 the bears move around

⭐ the bears go shopping

⬤ the bears are outside

Copyright © Pearson Education, Inc., or its affiliates. All Rights Reserved.

COMMON CORE STATE STANDARDS

Literature 1. Ask and answer questions about key details in a text. **Literature 3.** Describe characters, settings, and major events in a story, using key details. **Speaking/Listening 2.** Ask and answer questions about key details in a text read aloud or information presented orally or through other media.

Next

2. Part A

What do Bonnie Bear and Betty Bear do at the beginning of the story?

🍎 They go to the library.

⭐ They buy hats at the hat shop.

⚫ They make a list of errands.

Part B

Which detail from the story helps you know what Bonnie Bear and Betty Bear do at the beginning of the story?

🍎 Today they sat down to make a list

⭐ Then the bears went to their favorite hat shop.

⚫ Bonnie tried on a pale blue hat.

Copyright © Pearson Education, Inc., or its affiliates. All Rights Reserved.

COMMON CORE STATE STANDARDS

Literature 1. Ask and answer questions about key details in a text. **Literature 3.** Describe characters, settings, and major events in a story, using key details. **Speaking/Listening 2.** Ask and answer questions about key details in a text read aloud or information presented orally or through other media.

Next

Name _____

Vocabulary

Directions: Read aloud each question below and have children choose the best answer.

3. Part A

Nouns name people, animals, places, and things. Which of the following nouns names a place?

🍎 friends

⭐ library

⚫ hat

Part B

Which detail from the story helps you know which noun names a place?

🍎 had to go to the library

⭐ like different kinds of hats

⚫ were neighbors and good friends

COMMON CORE STATE STANDARDS

Language 1.b. Use common, proper, and possessive nouns. **Language 4.** Determine or clarify the meaning of unknown and multiple-meaning words and phrases based on *grade 1 reading and content*, choosing flexibly from an array of strategies. **Language 4.a.** Use sentence-level context as a clue to the meaning of a word or phrase. **Language 5.a.** Sort words into categories (e.g., colors, clothing) to gain a sense of the concepts the categories represent.

Next

Copyright © Pearson Education, Inc., or its affiliates. All Rights Reserved.

4. Part A

"When they found books they liked, they checked them out."
What do the words "checked them out" mean in the story?

🍎 hid them behind other books

⭐ paid what was owed when leaving

⚫ borrowed from a library

Part B

Which detail from the story helps you know what the words
"checked them out" mean?

🍎 we are such good friends

⭐ When they found books they liked . . .

⚫ "Yes, I suppose it is"

Copyright © Pearson Education, Inc., or its affiliates. All Rights Reserved.

COMMON CORE STATE STANDARDS

Language 4. Determine or clarify the meaning of unknown and multiple-meaning words and phrases based on *grade 1 reading and content,* choosing flexibly from an array of strategies. **Language 4.a.** Use sentence-level context as a clue to the meaning of a word or phrase.

Next

Name _____

Writing — Constructed Response

In the story "A Busy Day," Bonnie and Betty are good friends who like different things. Imagine Betty and Bonnie go to a flower shop. What kind of flowers does Betty like? What kind of flowers does Bonnie like? Complete these sentences to add to the story. Use color words to describe the flowers.

_____

Then the Bears went to _____.

_____

Betty liked the _____.

_____

Bonnie liked the _____.

"Isn't it curious that we are such good friends, yet we like

_____

different kinds of _____?"
asked Betty.

To the Teacher: Use the Writing Rubric on page T19 to assess children's writing.

COMMON CORE STATE STANDARDS

Literature 1. Ask and answer questions about key details in a text. **Literature 7.** Use illustrations and details in a story to describe its characters, setting, or events. **Writing 1.** Write opinion pieces in which they introduce the topic or name the book they are writing about, state an opinion, supply a reason for the opinion, and provide some sense of closure. **Language 1.f.** Use frequently occurring adjectives.

Copyright © Pearson Education, Inc., or its affiliates. All Rights Reserved.

Next

Writing — Extended Response

You have listened to or read two stories about places in neighborhoods.

- "A Busy Day"
- *Farmers Market*

In both stories, the characters visit places in their neighborhoods. Did you like one story better than the other? Write sentences telling why you liked the one story better. Use information from the stories to support your opinion. Use the story titles in your sentences. Begin every sentence with a capital letter. End each sentence with an end mark.

Copyright © Pearson Education, Inc., or its affiliates. All Rights Reserved.

To the Teacher: Tell children they may use the space on this page to plan their writing. Then have them write their response on the following pages. Use the Writing Rubric on page T20 to assess children's writing.

COMMON CORE STATE STANDARDS

Literature 7. Use illustrations and details in a story to describe its characters, setting, or events. **Writing 1.** Write opinion pieces in which they introduce the topic or name the book they are writing about, state an opinion, supply a reason for the opinion, and provide some sense of closure. **Language 2.** Demonstrate command of the conventions of standard English capitalization, punctuation, and spelling when writing.

Next

Name _____

Copyright © Pearson Education, Inc., or its affiliates. All Rights Reserved.

Copyright © Pearson Education, Inc., or its affiliates. All Rights Reserved.

Name _____

Copyright © Pearson Education, Inc., or its affiliates. All Rights Reserved.

Directions: Read aloud the following passage to children. Then read aloud each test item.

A Hamster for Ana

Ana wanted a hamster more than anything else in the world. Her friend Beth, who lived in the apartment upstairs, had a hamster named Harry. Harry was brown and white, and he loved to munch carrots from Beth's hand.

"Mom," Ana begged one day, "can I *please* get a hamster for my birthday next month? I don't want anything else!"

"Ana," her mother said, "having a pet is a big responsibility. Pets have lots of needs. A hamster needs shelter, and do you know what it eats and drinks?"

Ana *did* know. She had paid close attention to how Beth took care of Harry. She just needed a way to show her mom that she was ready for a pet.

The next week, Beth told Ana her family was going out of town. She asked if Ana could take care of Harry while she was away. Ana's mom said it was OK. This was just the chance Ana needed! She could show her mom that she could take care of a hamster.

Next

Every day for a whole week, Ana fed Harry. She kept his water bottle full and his cage clean. She gave him carrots to munch from her hand. Ana's mom gave him carrots to munch too. Ana was so happy that she gave her mom an extra-tight hug.

When Beth got home and came to take Harry back, Ana felt like crying. Ana's mom was sad too. Ana could hardly believe her ears when her mom said, "Let's take the city bus to the pet store downtown to get your birthday present, honey. It's time you had a hamster of your own."

Copyright © Pearson Education, Inc., or its affiliates. All Rights Reserved.

Name _____

Text-Based Comprehension

Directions: Read aloud each question below and have children choose the best answer.

1. Part A

Where does the story take place?

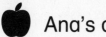 Ana's apartment

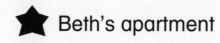 Beth's apartment

● the pet shop

Part B

Which detail from the story helps you know where the story takes place?

 Ana wanted a hamster more than anything

 Beth, who lived in the apartment upstairs

 "Let's take the city bus to the pet store downtown"

COMMON CORE STATE STANDARDS

Literature 1. Ask and answer questions about key details in a text. **Literature 3.** Describe characters, settings, and major events in a story, using key details. **Speaking/Listening 2.** Ask and answer questions about key details in a text read aloud or information presented orally or through other media.

Copyright © Pearson Education, Inc., or its affiliates. All Rights Reserved.

Next

2. Part A

How does Ana feel when Beth comes to get Harry?

 angry

 sad

⬤ surprised

Part B

Which detail in the story helps you know how Ana feels when Beth comes to get Harry?

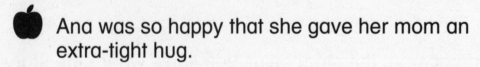 Ana was so happy that she gave her mom an extra-tight hug.

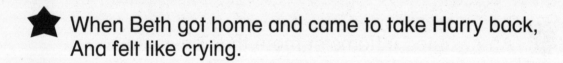 When Beth got home and came to take Harry back, Ana felt like crying.

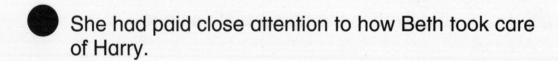 She had paid close attention to how Beth took care of Harry.

Copyright © Pearson Education, Inc., or its affiliates. All Rights Reserved.

COMMON CORE STATE STANDARDS

Literature 1. Ask and answer questions about key details in a text. **Literature 3.** Describe characters, settings, and major events in a story, using key details. **Speaking/Listening 2.** Ask and answer questions about key details in a text read aloud or information presented orally or through other media.

 Next

Vocabulary

Directions: Read aloud each question below and have children choose the best answer.

3. Part A

"This was just the chance Ana needed!" What does the word "chance" mean in the story?

 possibility

 risk

 opportunity

Part B

Which detail from the story helps you understand the meaning of the word "chance"?

 She could show her mom that she could take care of a hamster.

 The next week, Beth told Ana her family was going out of town.

 When Beth got home and came to take Harry back, Ana felt like crying.

COMMON CORE STATE STANDARDS

Literature 4. Identify words and phrases in stories or poems that suggest feelings or appeal to the senses.
Language 4. Determine or clarify the meaning of unknown and multiple-meaning words and phrases based on *grade 1 reading and content,* choosing flexibly from an array of strategies. **Language 4.a.** Use sentence-level context as a clue to the meaning of a word or phrase.

Next

Copyright © Pearson Education, Inc., or its affiliates. All Rights Reserved.

4. Part A

"She gave him carrots to munch from her hand." What does the word "munch" mean in the story?

 sweep

 eat

 drink

Part B

Which detail from the following sentence helps you know what the word "munch" means?

"She gave him carrots to munch from her hand."

 gave

 carrots

 hand

Copyright © Pearson Education, Inc., or its affiliates. All Rights Reserved.

COMMON CORE STATE STANDARDS

Literature 4. Identify words and phrases in stories or poems that suggest feelings or appeal to the senses.
Language 4. Determine or clarify the meaning of unknown and multiple-meaning words and phrases based on *grade 1 reading and content*, choosing flexibly from an array of strategies. **Language 4.a.** Use sentence-level context as a clue to the meaning of a word or phrase.

Next

Writing — Constructed Response

In the story, Ana shows Mom that she could take care of a pet. What did Ana do to show Mom she could care for a pet? Write two sentences that tell what Ana did for Harry, the hamster.

_____
- -
_____
- -
_____
- -
_____
- -
_____
- -
_____
- -
_____
- -
_____

Copyright © Pearson Education, Inc., or its affiliates. All Rights Reserved.

To the Teacher: Use the Writing Rubric on page T19 to assess children's writing.

COMMON CORE STATE STANDARDS

Literature 1. Ask and answer questions about key details in a text. **Writing 2.** Write informative/ explanatory texts in which they name a topic, supply some facts about the topic, and provide some sense of closure.

Next

Writing — Extended Response

You have listened to or read two stories about pets.

- "A Hamster for Ana"
- *Sam, Come Back!*

Think about the two pets. Would you rather have Sam or Harry as a pet? Give reasons for your opinion. Use information from the stories in your sentences. Begin each sentence with a capital letter. End each sentence with an end mark.

Copyright © Pearson Education, Inc., or its affiliates. All Rights Reserved.

To the Teacher: Tell children they may use the space on this page to plan their writing. Then have them write their response on the following pages. Use the Writing Rubric on page T20 to assess children's writing.

COMMON CORE STATE STANDARDS

Literature 1. Ask and answer questions about key details in a text. **Writing 1.** Write opinion pieces in which they introduce the topic or name the book they are writing about, state an opinion, supply a reason for the opinion, and provide some sense of closure. **Language 2.** Demonstrate command of the conventions of standard English capitalization, punctuation, and spelling when writing. **Language 2.b.** Use end punctuation for sentences.

Next

Name _____

_____

- -

_____

- -

_____

_____

- -

_____

_____

- -

_____

- -

_____

_____

- -

_____

- -

_____

- -

_____

- -

_____

Copyright © Pearson Education, Inc., or its affiliates. All Rights Reserved.

Next

Copyright © Pearson Education, Inc., or its affiliates. All Rights Reserved.

Name _____

**Directions: Read aloud the following passage to children.
Then read aloud each test item.**

Paws and Jake

"Paws! Jake! Where are you?" Marta called from the back door. She didn't see her puppies anywhere in the backyard. Suddenly, two furry pups ran out of her mother's garden. They were covered in dirt! . . .

Marta brought her puppies inside and turned on the bathwater. She made sure the water wasn't too hot. In went Paws. In went Jake. Marta washed both of them while they splashed and played.

Once Marta dried the pups, she saw how tangled their hair was. "My goodness," said Marta. "This won't do at all." She found the dog brush and used it as a tool to get all the tangles out. "I could have a career as a groomer!" giggled Marta.

After Marta finished brushing them, Paws and Jake looked like their old selves again. Paws jumped up and down and Jake began running in circles.

"You both certainly have a lot of energy!" said Marta. "Would you like to go for a walk?"

Copyright © Pearson Education, Inc., or its affiliates. All Rights Reserved.

Next

Paws and Jake bounced up and down as if to say, "Yes! Yes!"

Marta put their leashes on and took them out for a long walk around the block. As she walked, Marta thought about starting her own dog sitting service. She could take care of other people's dogs for a small fee. That would give her extra money to buy treats and toys for Paws and Jake.

Marta liked her idea so much that she wanted to run home to tell her mother. "Paws! Jake! I'll race you home!" she shouted playfully.

Copyright © Pearson Education, Inc., or its affiliates. All Rights Reserved.

Next

Name _____

Text-Based Comprehension

Directions: Read aloud each question below and have children choose the best answer.

1. Part A

What problem does Marta have with the puppies?

🍎 The puppies are not in the yard.

⭐ The puppies are very dirty.

⬤ The puppies destroy the garden.

Part B

Which detail from the story helps you know the problem Marta has with the puppies?

🍎 She didn't see her puppies anywhere

⭐ pups ran out of her mother's garden

⬤ They were covered in dirt!

Copyright © Pearson Education, Inc., or its affiliates. All Rights Reserved.

COMMON CORE STATE STANDARDS

Literature 1. Ask and answer questions about key details in a text. **Literature 3.** Describe characters, settings, and major events in a story, using key details. **Speaking/Listening 2.** Ask and answer questions about key details in a text read aloud or information presented orally or through other media.

Next

2. Part A

A summary tells the big idea of a paragraph or a story. Listen to the third paragraph from the story. What is the best summary of the paragraph?

🍎 Marta thinks she could have a career as a dog groomer.

⭐ The puppies have tangled hair, so Marta brushes them.

⬤ After Marta sees that the puppies have tangled hair, she finds the dog brush.

Part B

Which detail from the story helps you know which is the best summary of the paragraph?

🍎 "My goodness," said Marta. "This won't do at all."

⭐ "I could have a career as a groomer!" giggled Marta.

⬤ She found the dog brush and used it as a tool to get all the tangles out.

Copyright © Pearson Education, Inc., or its affiliates. All Rights Reserved.

COMMON CORE STATE STANDARDS

Literature 1. Ask and answer questions about key details in a text. **Literature 3.** Describe characters, settings, and major events in a story, using key details. **Speaking/Listening 2.** Ask and answer questions about key details in a text read aloud or information presented orally or through other media.

Next

Name _____

Vocabulary

Directions: Read aloud each question below and have children choose the best answer.

3. Part A

"Paws and Jake bounced up and down as if to say, Yes! Yes!" What does the word "bounced" mean in the story?

🍎 ran

⭐ wagged

⬤ jumped

Part B

Which words from the following sentence help you know what the word "bounced" means?

"Paws and Jake bounced up and down as if to say, Yes! Yes!"

🍎 Paws and Jake

⭐ up and down

⬤ Yes! Yes!

COMMON CORE STATE STANDARDS

Language 4. Determine or clarify the meaning of unknown and multiple-meaning words and phrases based on *grade 1 reading and content,* choosing flexibly from an array of strategies. **Language 4.a.** Use sentence-level context as a clue to the meaning of a word or phrase.

Copyright © Pearson Education, Inc., or its affiliates. All Rights Reserved.

Next

4. Part A

"She could take care of other people's dogs for a small fee."
What does the word "fee" mean in the story?

🍎 a small amount of time

⭐ food given to animals

⬤ money that pays for a service

Part B

Which detail from the story helps you know what the word "fee" means?

🍎 As she walked, Marta thought about starting her own dog sitting service.

⭐ That would give her extra money to buy treats and toys for Paws and Jake.

⬤ Marta liked her idea so much that she wanted to run home to tell her mother.

Copyright © Pearson Education, Inc., or its affiliates. All Rights Reserved.

COMMON CORE STATE STANDARDS

Language 4. Determine or clarify the meaning of unknown and multiple-meaning words and phrases based on *grade 1 reading and content,* choosing flexibly from an array of strategies. **Language 4.a.** Use sentence-level context as a clue to the meaning of a word or phrase.

Next

Name _____

Writing — Constructed Response

Good pet owners take care of their pets. Is Marta a good pet owner? Write sentences that tell what kind of pet owner Marta is. Use information from the story in your sentences.

_____

- -

_____

- -

_____

- -

_____

- -

_____

- -

_____

- -

_____

- -

_____

- -

Copyright © Pearson Education, Inc., or its affiliates. All Rights Reserved.

To the Teacher: Use the Writing Rubric on page T19 to assess children's writing.

COMMON CORE STATE STANDARDS

Literature 1. Ask and answer questions about key details in a text. **Writing 2.** Write informative/ explanatory texts in which they name a topic, supply some facts about the topic, and provide some sense of closure.

Next

Writing — Extended Response

You have listened to or read two stories about pets.

- "Paws and Jake"
- *Pig in a Wig*

Which story did you like better? Write sentences telling why you liked one story better than the other. Use information from the stories to support your opinion. Begin every sentence with a capital letter. End each sentence with an end mark.

Copyright © Pearson Education, Inc., or its affiliates. All Rights Reserved.

To the Teacher: Tell children they may use the space on this page to plan their writing. Then have them write their response on the following pages. Use the Writing Rubric on page T20 to assess children's writing.

COMMON CORE STATE STANDARDS

Literature 1. Ask and answer questions about key details in a text. **Writing 1.** Write opinion pieces in which they introduce the topic or name the book they are writing about, state an opinion, supply a reason for the opinion, and provide some sense of closure. **Language 2.** Demonstrate command of the conventions of standard English capitalization, punctuation, and spelling when writing. **Language 2.b.** Use end punctuation for sentences.

Next

Name _____

Copyright © Pearson Education, Inc., or its affiliates. All Rights Reserved.

Next

Copyright © Pearson Education, Inc., or its affiliates. All Rights Reserved.

Name _____

Directions: Read aloud the following passage to children.
Then read aloud each test item.

A Perfect Visit

Farmer Bob was very excited. His oldest, most favorite friend was coming to visit. Farmer Bob wanted everything to be just perfect. He pulled the weeds from the vegetable garden and painted the farmhouse bright white. "I want this place in tip-top shape," said Farmer Bob.

The animals in the barnyard watched as Farmer Bob worked and worked all day. That night, Farmer Bob went to the barn to feed the animals. He looked exhausted.

"Why are you working so hard, Farmer Bob?" asked Ox.

"My friend Bill is coming to visit. I want everything to be perfect." A tired Farmer Bob shuffled back to the farmhouse.

"There must be something we can do to help Farmer Bob," said Ox.

After a moment, Hen said, "I can collect eggs from the other hens and bake a cake. The hens will be happy to produce them."

Copyright © Pearson Education, Inc., or its affiliates. All Rights Reserved.

Next

"I can sweep out the barn with my tail," called Horse.

"I can pick flowers from the meadow and decorate the barnyard!" exclaimed Pig.

"Can I help too?" asked Cat.

"Yes," said Ox. "Farmer Bob and his friend will need transportation. You can help me fix up my cart."

The animals worked and worked through the night. "Oh, my!" Farmer Bob exclaimed in the morning. "The farm looks better than it ever has in the past. Who could have done all this work?"

The animals smiled as Farmer Bob filled their food bowls. "This will be the perfect visit," they all said.

Copyright © Pearson Education, Inc., or its affiliates. All Rights Reserved.

Next

Name _____

Text-Based Comprehension

Directions: Read aloud each question below and have children choose the best answer.

I. Part A

Where does the story take place?

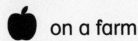 on a farm

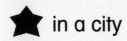 in a city

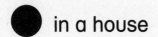 in a house

Part B

Which detail from the story helps you know where the story takes place?

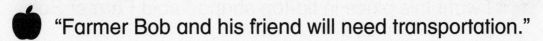 "Farmer Bob and his friend will need transportation."

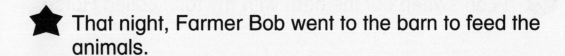 That night, Farmer Bob went to the barn to feed the animals.

⬤ His oldest, most favorite friend was coming to visit.

COMMON CORE STATE STANDARDS

Literature 3. Describe characters, settings, and major events in a story, using key details. **Literature 7.** Use illustrations and details in a story to describe its characters, setting, or events. **Speaking/Listening 2.** Ask and answer questions about key details in a text read aloud or information presented orally or through other media.

Copyright © Pearson Education, Inc., or its affiliates. All Rights Reserved.

Next

2. Part A

Which character in the story cleans the barn?

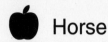 Horse

 Farmer Bob

● Ox

Part B

Which detail from the story helps you know which character cleans the barn?

 "There must be something we can do to help Farmer Bob," said Ox.

★ "I want this place in tip-top shape," said Farmer Bob.

● "I can sweep out the barn with my tail," called Horse.

Copyright © Pearson Education, Inc., or its affiliates. All Rights Reserved.

COMMON CORE STATE STANDARDS

Literature 3. Describe characters, settings, and major events in a story, using key details. **Literature 7.** Use illustrations and details in a story to describe its characters, setting, or events. **Speaking/Listening 2.** Ask and answer questions about key details in a text read aloud or information presented orally or through other media.

Next

Vocabulary

Directions: Read aloud each question below and have children choose the best answer.

3. Part A

"I want this place in tip-top shape," said Farmer Bob. What does the word "tip-top" mean in the story?

🍎 excellent

⭐ nice

⬤ messy

Part B

Which detail from the story provides a clue to the meaning of "tip-top"?

🍎 Farmer Bob worked and worked all day.

⭐ Farmer Bob wanted everything to be just perfect.

⬤ His oldest, most favorite friend was coming to visit.

Copyright © Pearson Education, Inc., or its affiliates. All Rights Reserved.

COMMON CORE STATE STANDARDS

Language 4. Determine or clarify the meaning of unknown and multiple-meaning words and phrases based on *grade 1 reading and content,* choosing flexibly from an array of strategies. **Language 4.a.** Use sentence-level context as a clue to the meaning of a word or phrase. **Language 5.** With guidance and support from adults, demonstrate understanding of word relationships and nuances in word meanings.

Next

4. Part A

The story says that Farmer Bob looked exhausted when he went to feed the animals at night. What word has almost the same meaning as "exhausted"?

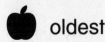 oldest

 hard

 tired

Part B

Which detail from the story helps you know which word has almost the same meaning as "exhausted"?

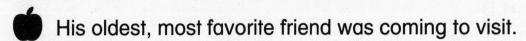 His oldest, most favorite friend was coming to visit.

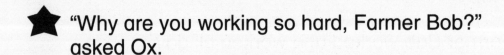 "Why are you working so hard, Farmer Bob?" asked Ox.

 A tired Farmer Bob shuffled back to the farmhouse.

Copyright © Pearson Education, Inc., or its affiliates. All Rights Reserved.

COMMON CORE STATE STANDARDS

Language 4. Determine or clarify the meaning of unknown and multiple-meaning words and phrases based on *grade 1 reading and content,* choosing flexibly from an array of strategies. **Language 4.a.** Use sentence-level context as a clue to the meaning of a word or phrase. **Language 5.** With guidance and support from adults, demonstrate understanding of word relationships and nuances in word meanings.

 Next

Name _____

Writing — Constructed Response

The story is about animals that help Farmer Bob get his farm in tip-top shape. Could this story really happen? Write two sentences explaining why it could or could not happen. Use details from the story in your answer.

_____
_____
_____
_____
_____
_____
_____
_____
_____
_____
_____
_____
_____
_____
_____
_____

Copyright © Pearson Education, Inc., or its affiliates. All Rights Reserved.

To the Teacher: Use the Writing Rubric on page T19 to assess children's writing.

COMMON CORE STATE STANDARDS

Literature 1. Ask and answer questions about key details in a text. **Literature 7.** Use illustrations and details in a story to describe its characters, setting, or events. **Literature 9.** Compare and contrast the adventures and experiences of characters in stories. **Writing 2.** Write informative/explanatory texts in which they name a topic, supply some facts about the topic, and provide some sense of closure.

Next

Writing — Extended Response

You have listened to or read two stories about animals.

- "A Perfect Visit"
- *The Big Blue Ox*

An ox is a main character in both stories. What does each ox do? How is what the oxen do alike? How is it different? Write sentences comparing what the oxen do. Use information from the stories in your sentences.

Copyright © Pearson Education, Inc., or its affiliates. All Rights Reserved.

To the Teacher: Tell children they may use the space on this page to plan their writing. Then have them write their response on the following pages. Use the Writing Rubric on page T20 to assess children's writing.

COMMON CORE STATE STANDARDS

Literature 1. Ask and answer questions about key details in a text. **Literature 7.** Use illustrations and details in a story to describe its characters, setting, or events. **Writing 2.** Write informative/explanatory texts in which they name a topic, supply some facts about the topic, and provide some sense of closure.

Next

Name _____

_____

- -

_____

- -

_____

- -

_____

- -

_____

- -

_____

- -

_____

_____

- -

_____

_____

- -

_____

_____

- -

_____

_____

- -

_____

Copyright © Pearson Education, Inc., or its affiliates. All Rights Reserved.

Next

Copyright © Pearson Education, Inc., or its affiliates. All Rights Reserved.

Name _____

**Directions: Read aloud the following passage to children.
Then read aloud each test item.**

A Caring Father

You are in cold, icy Antarctica. You see an odd sight.
It is a group of father penguins. They are caring for
penguin eggs.

Emperor penguins are the largest penguins. In
winter a mother penguin lays an egg. Then she goes
away. She looks for food. The father penguin stays there.
He cares for the egg.

The father puts its egg on its feet. He covers it with
warm skin. Several father penguins stand in a group.
One father waddles to the center. He warms up there.
Then another penguin father takes his place.

After about 65 days, the mother birds bring food.
They feed the new chicks. Then the fathers go for food.
Penguin parents care for their babies together.

Copyright © Pearson Education, Inc., or its affiliates. All Rights Reserved.

Next

Text-Based Comprehension

Directions: Read aloud each question below and have children choose the best answer.

I. Part A

What is the main idea of the passage "A Caring Father"?

🍎 Mother penguins lay eggs.

⭐ Emperor penguins are very large.

⬤ Father penguins care for the eggs.

Part B

Which detail from the story helps you know the main idea?

🍎 You see an odd sight.

⭐ He cares for the egg.

⬤ They feed the new chicks.

Copyright © Pearson Education, Inc., or its affiliates. All Rights Reserved.

COMMON CORE STATE STANDARDS

Informational Text 1. Ask and answer questions about key details in a text. **Informational Text 2.** Identify the main topic and retell key details of a text. **Speaking/Listening 2.** Ask and answer questions about key details in a text read aloud or information presented orally or through other media.

Next

Name _____

2. Part A

What is an important idea about penguin parents that the story provides?

🍎 One penguin parent always stays with the egg or chick.

⭐ Penguin fathers take care of the eggs, but not the chicks.

⬤ Penguin fathers stand in groups to help each other stay warm.

Part B

Which detail from the passage helps you know an important idea about the penguin parents?

🍎 Several father penguins stand in a group. One father waddles to the center.

⭐ Then she goes away. She looks for food. The father penguin stays there.

⬤ Emperor penguins are the largest penguins.

Copyright © Pearson Education, Inc., or its affiliates. All Rights Reserved.

COMMON CORE STATE STANDARDS

Informational Text 1. Ask and answer questions about key details in a text. **Informational Text 2.** Identify the main topic and retell key details of a text. **Speaking/Listening 2.** Ask and answer questions about key details in a text read aloud or information presented orally or through other media.

Next

Vocabulary

Directions: Read aloud each question below and have children choose the best answer.

3. Part A

"One father waddles to the center." What does the word "waddles" mean in the passage?

 sleeps

 eats

 walks

Part B

Which detail from the passage best helps you know what the word "waddles" means?

 After about 65 days, the mother birds bring food.

 Then another penguin father takes his place.

 It is a group of father penguins.

Copyright © Pearson Education, Inc., or its affiliates. All Rights Reserved.

COMMON CORE STATE STANDARDS

Informational Text 4. Ask and answer questions to help determine or clarify the meaning of words and phrases in a text. **Language 4.** Determine or clarify the meaning of unknown and multiple-meaning words and phrases based on *grade 1 reading and content*, choosing flexibly from an array of strategies. **Language 4.a.** Use sentence-level context as a clue to the meaning of a word or phrase.

4. Part A

"The father puts its egg on its feet. He covers it with warm skin." What does the word "covers" mean in the passage?

🍎 includes something

⭐ puts something over

⬤ blankets or quilts

Part B

Which detail from the following sentences helps you know what the word "covers" means?

"The father puts its egg on its feet. He covers it with warm skin."

🍎 the father puts

⭐ on its feet

⬤ with warm skin

Copyright © Pearson Education, Inc., or its affiliates. All Rights Reserved.

COMMON CORE STATE STANDARDS

Informational Text 4. Ask and answer questions to help determine or clarify the meaning of words and phrases in a text. **Language 4.** Determine or clarify the meaning of unknown and multiple-meaning words and phrases based on *grade 1 reading and content,* choosing flexibly from an array of strategies. **Language 4.a.** Use sentence-level context as a clue to the meaning of a word or phrase.

Next

Writing – Constructed Response

Write sentences that explain why father penguins take care of the eggs. Use information from the passage in your sentences.

_____
- -
_____
- -
_____
- -
_____
- -
_____
- -
_____
- -
_____

To the Teacher: Use the Writing Rubric on page T19 to assess children's writing.

COMMON CORE STATE STANDARDS

Informational Text 1. Ask and answer questions about key details in a text. **Writing 2.** Write informative/ explanatory texts in which they name a topic, supply some facts about the topic, and provide some sense of closure.

Next

Copyright © Pearson Education, Inc., or its affiliates. All Rights Reserved.

Name _____

_____

_____

_____

_____

_____

_____

_____

_____

_____

_____

_____

_____

_____

_____

_____

_____

Copyright © Pearson Education, Inc., or its affiliates. All Rights Reserved.

Writing — Extended Response

You have listened to or read two selections about animals.

- "A Caring Father"
- *A Fox and a Kit*

Both "A Caring Father" and *A Fox and a Kit* tell about animals caring for their young. How do the adult and baby animals get food? Write sentences that tell how the animals in each selection get food. Also tell why the way they get food is different. Use the story titles in your sentences.

Copyright © Pearson Education, Inc., or its affiliates. All Rights Reserved.

To the Teacher: Tell children they may use the space on this page to plan their writing. Then have them write their response on the following pages. Use the Writing Rubric on page T20 to assess children's writing.

COMMON CORE STATE STANDARDS

Informational Text 1. Ask and answer questions about key details in a text. **Writing 2.** Write informative/explanatory texts in which they name a topic, supply some facts about the topic, and provide some sense of closure.

Next

Name _____

_____
- -
_____

_____
- -
_____

_____
- -
_____

_____
- -
_____

_____
- -
_____

_____
- -
_____

_____
- -
_____

_____
- -
_____

_____
- -

Copyright © Pearson Education, Inc., or its affiliates. All Rights Reserved.

Copyright © Pearson Education, Inc., or its affiliates. All Rights Reserved.

Stop

Name _____

**Directions: Read aloud the following passage to children.
Then read aloud each test item.**

The Pecking Hen

Grandma Bess lived in a big, old, white house in the country. Kashia, who lived in the city, always learned something new when she visited her grandmother.

Grandma Bess had a wonderful garden. She planted tomatoes, carrots, okra, corn, and green beans. Kashia loved to help her grandmother pick the fresh vegetables. It was like shopping at the grocery store for free!

Grandma Bess also had a pen where she kept hens. Each morning, she went inside the pen and gathered eggs. One morning, Kashia went with her. Kashia saw a huge white hen sitting on a nest, waiting for her eggs to hatch. Kashia bent her head near the hen to get a better look.

Peck! Peck! Squawk! Squawk!

"Ouch!" cried Kashia.

Grandma Bess turned to Kashia quickly and said, "What's wrong?"

"The hen pecked me on the nose! It hurts!"

Copyright © Pearson Education, Inc., or its affiliates. All Rights Reserved.

Next

Grandma Bess chuckled. "That's what a hen does to survive. She protects herself and her habitat from danger."

"It's not funny!" Kashia said. "And I'm not dangerous!"

"No, you're not, Kashia, but the hen doesn't know that. The same thing happened to me when I was your age. I got too close to a hen too. It pecked me right on the nose," said Grandma Bess. "Hens use their beaks to protect themselves and their eggs."

"I guess I learned my lesson," Kashia said. "From now on, I'll keep my nose out of the hen's business!"

Grandma Bess and Kashia laughed.

Copyright © Pearson Education, Inc., or its affiliates. All Rights Reserved.

Name _____

Text-Based Comprehension

Directions: Read aloud each question below and have children choose the best answer.

1. Part A

Where does the story take place?

 where Grandma Bess lives

 Kashia's home in the city

 inside an old white house

Part B

Which detail from the story helps you know where the story takes place?

 Grandma Bess lived in a big, old, white house in the country.

 Kashia bent her head near the hen to get a better look.

 Grandma Bess turned to Kashia quickly and said, "What's wrong?"

COMMON CORE STATE STANDARDS

Literature 3. Describe characters, settings, and major events in a story, using key details. **Literature 7.** Use illustrations and details in a story to describe its characters, setting, or events. **Speaking/Listening 2.** Ask and answer questions about key details in a text read aloud or information presented orally or through other media.

Next

Copyright © Pearson Education, Inc., or its affiliates. All Rights Reserved.

2. Part A

What is the story mostly about?

 Kashia visits Grandma Bess in the country.

 Grandma raises vegetables and hens in the country.

 Kashia learns how hens protect themselves.

Part B

Which detail from the story helps you know what the story is about?

 "The hen pecked me on the nose! It hurts!"

 "Hens use their beaks to protect themselves and their eggs."

 Kashia saw a huge white hen sitting on a nest, waiting for her eggs to hatch.

Copyright © Pearson Education, Inc., or its affiliates. All Rights Reserved.

COMMON CORE STATE STANDARDS

Literature 1. Ask and answer questions about key details in a text. **Literature 3.** Describe characters, settings, and major events in a story, using key details. **Speaking/Listening 2.** Ask and answer questions about key details in a text read aloud or information presented orally or through other media.

Next

Name _____

Vocabulary

Directions: Read aloud each question below and have children choose the best answer.

3. Part A

"Grandma Bess chuckled." What is the meaning of the word "chuckled" in the story?

 frowned

 cried

 laughed

Part B

Which detail from the story helps you know what the word "chuckled" means?

 "That's what a hen does"

 "It's not funny!"

 "What's wrong?"

Copyright © Pearson Education, Inc., or its affiliates. All Rights Reserved.

COMMON CORE STATE STANDARDS

Language 4. Determine or clarify the meaning of unknown and multiple-meaning words and phrases based on *grade 1 reading and content,* choosing flexibly from an array of strategies. **Language 4.a.** Use sentence-level context as a clue to the meaning of a word or phrase.

Next

4. Part A

"The hen pecked me on the nose!" What does the word "pecked" mean in the story?

 struck at with a beak

 quickly kissed

 picked up with a beak

Part B

Which detail from the story helps you understand the meaning of the word "pecked"?

 Squawk! Squawk!

 "It hurts!"

 "I guess I learned my lesson"

Copyright © Pearson Education, Inc., or its affiliates. All Rights Reserved.

COMMON CORE STATE STANDARDS

Language 4. Determine or clarify the meaning of unknown and multiple-meaning words and phrases based on *grade 1 reading and content,* choosing flexibly from an array of strategies. **Language 4.a.** Use sentence-level context as a clue to the meaning of a word or phrase.

Next

Name _____

Writing — Constructed Response

In the story "The Pecking Hen," Kashia always learns something when she visits Grandma Bess. What does Kashia learn about hens? Write sentences telling what she learns. Use information from the story in your sentences.

_____

_____

_____

_____

_____

_____

_____

_____

_____

_____

Copyright © Pearson Education, Inc., or its affiliates. All Rights Reserved.

To the Teacher: Use the Writing Rubric on page T19 to assess children's writing.

COMMON CORE STATE STANDARDS

Literature 1. Ask and answer questions about key details in a text. **Writing 2.** Write informative/explanatory texts in which they name a topic, supply some facts about the topic, and provide some sense of closure.

Next

Writing — Extended Response

You have listened to or read two stories about birds and eggs.

- "The Pecking Hen"
- *Get the Egg!*

Both "The Pecking Hen" and *Get the Egg!* are stories that tell about children's experiences with birds and eggs. How are the experiences of Kashia in "The Pecking Hen" like those of Kim and Brad in *Get the Egg!?* How are they different? Use information from the stories in your sentences.

Copyright © Pearson Education, Inc., or its affiliates. All Rights Reserved.

To the Teacher: Tell children they may use the space on this page to plan their writing. Then have them write their response on the following pages. Use the Writing Rubric on page T20 to assess children's writing.

COMMON CORE STATE STANDARDS

Literature 1. Ask and answer questions about key details in a text. **Literature 7.** Use illustrations and details in a story to describe its characters, setting, or events. **Literature 9.** Compare and contrast the adventures and experiences of characters in stories. **Writing 2.** Write informative/explanatory texts in which they name a topic, supply some facts about the topic, and provide some sense of closure.

Next

Name _____

Copyright © Pearson Education, Inc., or its affiliates. All Rights Reserved.

Next

Copyright © Pearson Education, Inc., or its affiliates. All Rights Reserved.

Directions: Read aloud the following passage to children.
Then read aloud each test item.

When Animals Are Doctors

USING MEDICINE

If you get sick or hurt, a doctor may treat you and give
you medicine to help you get better. Animals don't have
doctors. But some kinds "doctor" themselves.

Chimpanzees eat a lot of leaves and other plant parts.
Some have been seen swallowing bristly leaves whole.
As the leaves pass through a chimp's body, they act a bit
like a broom, "sweeping out" worms and other pests that
could make the animal sick.

A chimp can find a leaf from an aloe plant and break
it open. It can smear liquid from the leaf over a sore on
its foot. It may just use the leaf to wipe off the sore. But
some people use aloe to treat burns and scrapes. So
perhaps the chimp does that too. . . .

EAT DIRT

Elephants scoop up gobs of mud to eat. Why? Because
the mud contains lots of minerals. Usually, plants provide
the minerals that elephants need.

Copyright © Pearson Education, Inc., or its affiliates. All Rights Reserved.

Next

In some places where elephants live, the plants don't have enough minerals in them to keep the animals healthy. So the elephants have found a goopy way to get them.

BONE UP ON CALCIUM

Giraffes chew on bones to get a mineral called calcium. Rodents, gopher tortoises, and many other animals also nibble on old bones and antlers for the calcium they need.

Scientists are still discovering different tricks that animals use to doctor themselves. They wonder if some of these same tricks and medicines could help people. After all, everyone wants to stay healthy!

Copyright © Pearson Education, Inc., or its affiliates. All Rights Reserved.

Name _____

Text-Based Comprehension

Directions: Read aloud each question below and have children choose the best answer.

I. **Part A**

What effect does eating whole bristly leaves have on chimps?

🍎 It makes the chimpanzees feel weak and sick.

⭐ It gets rid of pests the chimps may have eaten.

⬤ It makes a chimp's sore foot heal more quickly.

Part B

Which detail from the story helps you know what effect eating whole bristly leaves has on chimps?

🍎 they act a bit like a broom, "sweeping out" worms and other pests that could make the animal sick

⭐ *Chimpanzees* eat a lot of leaves and other plant parts. Some have been seen swallowing bristly leaves whole.

⬤ But some people use aloe to treat burns and scrapes. So perhaps the chimp does that too.

Copyright © Pearson Education, Inc., or its affiliates. All Rights Reserved.

COMMON CORE STATE STANDARDS

Informational Text 1. Ask and answer questions about key details in a text. **Informational Text 3.** Describe the connection between two individuals, events, ideas, or pieces of information in a text. **Speaking/Listening 2.** Ask and answer questions about key details in a text read aloud or information presented orally or through other media.

Next

2. Part A

How do giraffes get the calcium they need?

🍎 They eat tree bark.

⭐ They chew on bones.

⬤ They eat mud.

Part B

Under which heading would you find the information you need to learn where giraffes get the calcium they need?

🍎 "USING MEDICINE"

⭐ "EAT DIRT"

⬤ "BONE UP ON CALCIUM"

Copyright © Pearson Education, Inc., or its affiliates. All Rights Reserved.

COMMON CORE STATE STANDARDS

Informational Text 1. Ask and answer questions about key details in a text. **Informational Text 5.** Know and use various text features (e.g., headings, tables of contents, glossaries, electronic menus, icons) to locate key facts or information in a text. **Speaking/Listening 2.** Ask and answer questions about key details in a text read aloud or information presented orally or through other media.

Next

Name _____

Vocabulary

Directions: Read aloud each question below and have children choose the best answer.

3. Part A

"It can smear liquid from the leaf over a sore on its foot."
What does the word "smear" mean in the selection?

 stain

 spread

 touch

Part B

Which detail from the selection helps you know what the word "smear" means?

 A chimp can find a leaf from an aloe plant and break it open.

 So perhaps the chimp does that too.

 It may just use the leaf to wipe off the sore.

COMMON CORE STATE STANDARDS

Informational Text 4. Ask and answer questions to help determine or clarify the meaning of words and phrases in a text. **Language 4.a.** Use sentence-level context as a clue to the meaning of a word or phrase. **Language 5.** With guidance and support from adults, demonstrate understanding of word relationships and nuances in word meanings.

Next

Copyright © Pearson Education, Inc., or its affiliates. All Rights Reserved.

4. Part A

"*Giraffes* chew on bones to get a mineral called calcium."
What word has almost the same meaning as "chew"?

🍎 need

⭐ nibble

⬤ treat

Part B

Which detail from the selection helps you know which word
has almost the same meaning as "chew"?

🍎 But some people use aloe to treat burns and scrapes.

⭐ many other animals also nibble on old bones

⬤ for the calcium they need

Copyright © Pearson Education, Inc., or its affiliates. All Rights Reserved.

COMMON CORE STATE STANDARDS

Informational Text 4. Ask and answer questions to help determine or clarify the meaning of words and
phrases in a text. **Language 4.a.** Use sentence-level context as a clue to the meaning of a word or phrase.
Language 5. With guidance and support from adults, demonstrate understanding of word relationships
and nuances in word meanings.

Next

Name _____

Writing – Constructed Response

In the selection "When Animals Are Doctors," you learned about some of the unusual things animals eat. Complete the following sentences to tell what the animals eat and to explain why they eat such unusual things.

Chimpanzees eat _____.

They eat them to _____.

Elephants eat _____.

They eat this to _____.

Copyright © Pearson Education, Inc., or its affiliates. All Rights Reserved.

To the Teacher: Use the Writing Rubric on page T19 to assess children's writing.

COMMON CORE STATE STANDARDS

Informational Text 1. Ask and answer questions about key details in a text. **Writing 2.** Write informative/explanatory texts in which they name a topic, supply some facts about the topic, and provide some sense of closure.

Next

Giraffes eat _____.

They eat this to _____.

Copyright © Pearson Education, Inc., or its affiliates. All Rights Reserved.

Next

Writing — Extended Response

You have listened to a text selection and read a poem about animals.

- "When Animals Are Doctors"
- "Raccoons"

Both the selection and the poem use the word "treat," but the word has different meanings. What does the word "treat" mean in the selection "When Animals Are Doctors"? What does the word "treat" mean in the poem "Raccoons"? Write sentences to explain the differences in the meaning of the word "treat." Use the titles of the selection and poem and information from them in your sentences.

Copyright © Pearson Education, Inc., or its affiliates. All Rights Reserved.

To the Teacher: Tell children they may use the space on this page to plan their writing. Then have them write their response on the following page. Use the Writing Rubric on page T20 to assess children's writing.

COMMON CORE STATE STANDARDS

Informational Text 4. Ask and answer questions to help determine or clarify the meaning of words and phrases in a text. **Writing 2.** Write informative/explanatory texts in which they name a topic, supply some facts about the topic, and provide some sense of closure. **Language 4.** Determine or clarify the meaning of unknown and multiple-meaning words and phrases based on *grade 1 reading and content,* choosing flexibly from an array of strategies.

Next

Copyright © Pearson Education, Inc., or its affiliates. All Rights Reserved.

Name _____

**Directions: Read aloud the following passage to children.
Then read aloud each test item.**

Annie Helps Out

It was Saturday morning. Al and Steven stared at the list of household chores stuck to the refrigerator door. They had to finish everything before they could go to the movies. "Wash the dog, clean the birdcage, weed the garden," Al read aloud. "We'll never make it to the movies," groaned Steven.

"I can help," said their sister Annie.

"You're too little to help," said Al.

"Little sisters just get in the way," said Steven.

"You'll see," Annie replied.

First, Al filled a bucket with sudsy water. Then he went to get the dog from the backyard. On his way back, he tripped over the bucket and spilled the sudsy water all over.

"I can help," called Annie. She filled the bucket with sudsy water again.

"Thanks, Annie!" exclaimed Al.

Copyright © Pearson Education, Inc., or its affiliates. All Rights Reserved.

Next

Steven cleaned the birdcage and then filled Tweety's bowl with birdseed. Just as Steven was finishing, Mr. Whiskers, the family cat, came along. He knocked the bag over, and birdseed spilled everywhere.

"I can help," called Annie. She swept up all the birdseed and put it back into the bag.

"Thanks, Annie!" exclaimed Steven.

Now it was time to weed the garden. Al and Steven pulled weeds. It was a hot afternoon, and the boys were tired. At last they were done.

Annie came outside. "I can help," she called. "Mom and I made lemonade! Come in and get some."

Al and Steven were thirsty. "Thanks, Annie!" they exclaimed.

"We were wrong, Annie," said Al. "You're not too little to help!"

"In fact, you were such a big help," said Steven, "we'll take you to the movies with us."

Copyright © Pearson Education, Inc., or its affiliates. All Rights Reserved.

Next

Name _____

Text-Based Comprehension

Directions: Read aloud each question below and have children choose the best answer.

I. **Part A**

What does Al do after he reads the list of chores?

 cleans the birdcage and feeds the bird

 makes lemonade with Annie

 fills a bucket with soapy water

Part B

Which detail from the story helps you know what Al does after he reads the list of chores?

 Steven cleaned the birdcage

 It was a hot afternoon, and the boys were tired.

 First, Al filled a bucket with sudsy water.

Copyright © Pearson Education, Inc., or its affiliates. All Rights Reserved.

COMMON CORE STATE STANDARDS

Literature 1. Ask and answer questions about key details in a text. **Literature 2.** Retell stories, including key details, and demonstrate understanding of their central message or lesson. **Literature 3.** Describe characters, settings, and major events in a story, using key details. **Speaking/Listening 2.** Ask and answer questions about key details in a text read aloud or information presented orally or through other media.

Next

2. Part A

What is the big idea of the story?

⬛ (apple) Steven and Al find they can do jobs faster without Annie's help.

⭐ Steven and Al learn that little sisters can be very helpful.

⚫ Steven and Al have too many chores to do on Saturday.

Part B

Which detail in the story helps you know the big idea of the story?

⬛ (apple) "We were wrong, Annie," said Al. "You're not too little to help!"

⭐ "Little sisters just get in the way," said Steven.

⚫ Annie came outside. "I can help," she called.

Copyright © Pearson Education, Inc., or its affiliates. All Rights Reserved.

COMMON CORE STATE STANDARDS

Literature 1. Ask and answer questions about key details in a text. **Literature 2.** Retell stories, including key details, and demonstrate understanding of their central message or lesson. **Literature 3.** Describe characters, settings, and major events in a story, using key details. **Speaking/Listening 2.** Ask and answer questions about key details in a text read aloud or information presented orally or through other media.

Next

Vocabulary

Directions: Read aloud each question below and have children choose the best answer.

3. **Part A**

A noun names people, places, things, or animals.
Which noun names things?

 birdseed

 cat

 sister

Part B

Which detail from the story helps you know which noun names things?

 "Little sisters just get in the way," said Steven.

 he tripped over the bucket and spilled the sudsy water all over

 She swept up all the birdseed and put it back into the bag.

COMMON CORE STATE STANDARDS

Language 4. Determine or clarify the meaning of unknown and multiple-meaning words and phrases based on *grade 1 reading and content,* choosing flexibly from an array of strategies. **Language 4.a.** Use sentence-level context as a clue to the meaning of a word or phrase. **Language 5.a.** Sort words into categories (e.g., colors, clothing) to gain a sense of the concepts the categories represent.

Copyright © Pearson Education, Inc., or its affiliates. All Rights Reserved.

Next

4. Part A

"Al and Steven stared at the list of household chores stuck to the refrigerator door." Which word is closest in meaning to the word "chores" in the story?

 play

 jobs

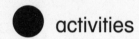 activities

Part B

Which detail from the story helps you understand the meaning of the word "chores"?

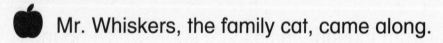 Mr. Whiskers, the family cat, came along.

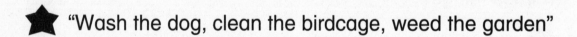 "Wash the dog, clean the birdcage, weed the garden"

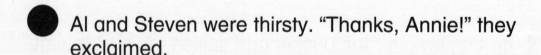 Al and Steven were thirsty. "Thanks, Annie!" they exclaimed.

Copyright © Pearson Education, Inc., or its affiliates. All Rights Reserved.

COMMON CORE STATE STANDARDS

Language 4. Determine or clarify the meaning of unknown and multiple-meaning words and phrases based on *grade 1 reading and content,* choosing flexibly from an array of strategies. **Language 4.a.** Use sentence-level context as a clue to the meaning of a word or phrase. **Language 5.** With guidance and support from adults, demonstrate understanding of word relationships and nuances in word meanings.

Next

Name _____

Writing — Constructed Response

In the story, Annie helps her brothers as they do their chores. How did she help her brothers? Write sentences that tell what Annie did to help. Put your sentences in the order they happen. Begin every sentence with a capital letter. End each sentence with an end mark.

_____

_____

_____

_____

_____

_____

_____

_____

_____

Copyright © Pearson Education, Inc., or its affiliates. All Rights Reserved.

To the Teacher: Use the Writing Rubric on page T19 to assess children's writing.

COMMON CORE STATE STANDARDS

Literature 1. Ask and answer questions about key details in a text. **Writing 3.** Write narratives in which they recount two or more appropriately sequenced events, include some details regarding what happened, use temporal words to signal event order, and provide some sense of closure. **Language 2.** Demonstrate command of the conventions of standard English capitalization, punctuation, and spelling when writing. **Language 2.b.** Use end punctuation for sentences.

Next

Writing — Extended Response

You have listened to or read two selections about families doing chores.

- "Annie Helps Out"
- "At Home"

Think about the chores the families do. Write sentences comparing the chores the two families do. How are the chores alike? How are they different? Use information from the selections in your sentences. Remember to begin every sentence with a capital letter. Be sure to end each sentence with an end mark.

To the Teacher: Tell children they may use the space on this page to plan their writing. Then have them write their response on the following pages. Use the Writing Rubric on page T20 to assess children's writing.

Copyright © Pearson Education, Inc., or its affiliates. All Rights Reserved.

COMMON CORE STATE STANDARDS

Literature 9. Compare and contrast the adventures and experiences of characters in stories. **Writing 2.** Write informative/explanatory texts in which they name a topic, supply some facts about the topic, and provide some sense of closure. **Language 2.** Demonstrate command of the conventions of standard English capitalization, punctuation, and spelling when writing. **Language 2.b.** Use end punctuation for sentences.

Next

Name _____

Copyright © Pearson Education, Inc., or its affiliates. All Rights Reserved.

Next

Copyright © Pearson Education, Inc., or its affiliates. All Rights Reserved.

Name _____

**Directions: Read aloud the following passage to children.
Then read aloud each test item.**

Jimmy's Lesson

"Wake up, Jimmy!" Jimmy's mother said. "Get up or you will be late to school!"

Jimmy was sleepy because he had stayed up late the night before reading his new book. His mom had warned him he would be tired if he stayed up too late. . . .

Jimmy jumped out of bed. He brushed his teeth, washed his face, and grabbed his backpack. Jimmy ran into the kitchen and quickly drank . . . orange juice. He gobbled up his eggs.

"We're out of time," said his mother. She grabbed the car keys. "Let's go!"

Jimmy and his mom arrived at school just as the warning bell rang. . . . His mother smiled and said, "Hope you learn a lot today."

Jimmy sat down at his desk. He looked inside his backpack. "Oh, no!" Jimmy exclaimed.

His pencils and crayons weren't there. His homework wasn't there either. "I was in such a hurry to leave that I forgot all my stuff!"

Copyright © Pearson Education, Inc., or its affiliates. All Rights Reserved.

Next

During art, a friend offered to share his crayons. During spelling, Jimmy had to borrow a pencil. And during math, Jimmy was the only one in his group who didn't have his homework.

Finally, the day was over. Jimmy was exhausted. When his mother picked him up, Jimmy got into the car and sighed. "I'm glad that's over!" he said.

"What?" his mother asked. "Did you learn something that was really hard today?"

. . . "I learned that I should go to bed on time so that I can get up on time. If I don't, I might leave in a hurry and forget everything I need for school."

"I think you learned a lot today," said Jimmy's mom with a smile.

Copyright © Pearson Education, Inc., or its affiliates. All Rights Reserved.

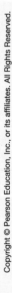
Next

Name _____

Text-Based Comprehension

Directions: Read aloud each question below and have children choose the best answer.

I. Part A

What caused Jimmy to be sleepy?

🍎 He had stayed up too late.

⭐ He got up earlier than usual.

⬤ He could not fall asleep the night before.

Part B

Which word from the following sentence gives a clue that helps you identify what caused Jimmy to be sleepy?

"Jimmy was sleepy because he had stayed up late the night before reading his new book."

🍎 sleepy

⭐ because

⬤ before

COMMON CORE STATE STANDARDS

Literature 1. Ask and answer questions about key details in a text. **Literature 2.** Retell stories, including key details, and demonstrate understanding of their central message or lesson. **Literature 3.** Describe characters, settings, and major events in a story, using key details. **Speaking/Listening 2.** Ask and answer questions about key details in a text read aloud or information presented orally or through other media.

Next

Copyright © Pearson Education, Inc., or its affiliates. All Rights Reserved.

2. Part A

Why does Jimmy say "Oh, no!" when he opens his backpack?

🍎 Things he needed were not in it.

⭐ His homework papers were torn.

⚫ He forgot to put his lunch in it.

Part B

Which detail from the story helps you know why Jimmy says "Oh, no!" when he opens his backpack?

🍎 He brushed his teeth, washed his face, and grabbed his backpack.

⭐ During art, a friend offered to share his crayons.

⚫ "I was in such a hurry to leave that I forgot all my stuff!"

Copyright © Pearson Education, Inc., or its affiliates. All Rights Reserved.

COMMON CORE STATE STANDARDS

Literature 1. Ask and answer questions about key details in a text. **Literature 2.** Retell stories, including key details, and demonstrate understanding of their central message or lesson. **Literature 3.** Describe characters, settings, and major events in a story, using key details. **Speaking/Listening 2.** Ask and answer questions about key details in a text read aloud or information presented orally or through other media.

Next

Name _____

Vocabulary

Directions: Read aloud each question below and have children choose the best answer.

3. Part A

"Jimmy ran into the kitchen and quickly drank . . . orange juice. He gobbled up his eggs." What does the word "gobbled" mean in the story?

🍎 took as one's own

⭐ sounded like a turkey

⬤ ate very fast

Part B

Which detail from the following sentences helps you know what the word "gobbled" means?

"Jimmy ran into the kitchen and quickly drank . . . orange juice. He gobbled up his eggs."

🍎 kitchen

⭐ quickly

⬤ drank

COMMON CORE STATE STANDARDS

Language 4. Determine or clarify the meaning of unknown and multiple-meaning words and phrases based on *grade 1 reading and content,* choosing flexibly from an array of strategies. **Language 4.a.** Use sentence-level context as a clue to the meaning of a word or phrase.

Copyright © Pearson Education, Inc., or its affiliates. All Rights Reserved.

Next

4. Part A

"Jimmy was sleepy because he had stayed up late the night before reading his new book." What word has almost the same meaning as the word "sleepy"?

 tired

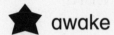 awake

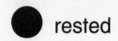 rested

Part B

Which words from the following sentence help you know which word has almost the same meaning as the word "sleepy"?

"Jimmy was sleepy because he had stayed up late the night before reading his new book."

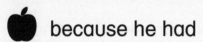 because he had

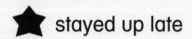 stayed up late

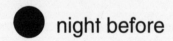 night before

Copyright © Pearson Education, Inc., or its affiliates. All Rights Reserved.

COMMON CORE STATE STANDARDS

Language 4. Determine or clarify the meaning of unknown and multiple-meaning words and phrases based on *grade 1 reading and content,* choosing flexibly from an array of strategies. **Language 4.a.** Use sentence-level context as a clue to the meaning of a word or phrase.

Next

Name _____

Writing — Constructed Response

Jimmy learned a lesson about staying up late. How will that lesson affect him? What will he do tonight? What will he do in the morning? Complete sentences telling what Jimmy will do tonight and tomorrow morning. Use information from the story to add a new ending to it.

_____

Tonight Jimmy _____.

_____

In the morning, he _____.

_____

Then he _____.

_____

He puts his things _____.

_____

He gets to school _____.

To the Teacher: Use the Writing Rubric on page T19 to assess children's writing.

COMMON CORE STATE STANDARDS

Literature 1. Ask and answer questions about key details in a text. **Writing 3.** Write narratives in which they recount two or more appropriately sequenced events, include some details regarding what happened, use temporal words to signal event order, and provide some sense of closure.

Copyright © Pearson Education, Inc., or its affiliates. All Rights Reserved.

Next

Writing — Extended Response

You have listened to or read two stories about children in school communities.

- "Jimmy's Lesson"
- *The Farmer in the Hat*

In school communities, people help each other and work together. How did children in the two stories help each other? Write sentences explaining how the schools in the story are communities. Use information from the stories in your sentences. Begin every sentence with a capital letter. End each sentence with an end mark.

Copyright © Pearson Education, Inc., or its affiliates. All Rights Reserved.

To the Teacher: Tell children they may use the space on this page to plan their writing. Then have them write their response on the following pages. Use the Writing Rubric on page T20 to assess children's writing.

COMMON CORE STATE STANDARDS

Literature 1. Ask and answer questions about key details in a text. **Writing 2.** Write informative/explanatory texts in which they name a topic, supply some facts about the topic, and provide some sense of closure. **Language 2.** Demonstrate command of the conventions of standard English capitalization, punctuation, and spelling when writing. **Language 2.b.** Use end punctuation for sentences.

Next

Name _____

_____

_____

_____

_____

_____

_____

_____

_____

_____

_____

_____

_____

_____

_____

_____

_____

_____

_____

Copyright © Pearson Education, Inc., or its affiliates. All Rights Reserved.

Next

Copyright © Pearson Education, Inc., or its affiliates. All Rights Reserved.

Name _____

**Directions: Read aloud the following passage to children.
Then read aloud each test item.**

How a City Grows

Long ago, where there's a big city now, there were once just meadows, and hills, and forests. What happened?

Like a person, a city starts out small—and grows. At first there were just a few houses or farms. There were no roads, just trails that deer or other animals followed. People traveled by horse or even canoe. But mainly they walked wherever they needed to go.

As more people came, some built their own farms. Others opened small stores. Some people became carpenters or blacksmiths. Others were workers who built houses, washed laundry, unloaded ships, or drove carts.

As the town grew, railroads and factories came— along with even more people looking for jobs. There are no cities without jobs for people to do to earn money for their families. With more families, the town needed schools and libraries and newspapers and banks. The city grew and grew.

Copyright © Pearson Education, Inc., or its affiliates. All Rights Reserved.

Next

Finally, the city was huge! Millions of people lived and worked in tall skyscrapers. The streets were crowded with cars and buses and trains. There were large, fancy stores and theaters and sports stadiums. Underground pipes brought water from the lake to the buildings, and wires carried electricity.

Now the city is very busy—and very exciting!

Copyright © Pearson Education, Inc., or its affiliates. All Rights Reserved.

Name _____

Text-Based Comprehension

Directions: Read aloud each question below and have children choose the best answer.

1. **Part A**

   What is the author's purpose for writing this selection?

   🍎 to entertain readers with a story about a person growing up in a city

   ★ to provide information about the way a city grows over time

   ● to give an opinion about large cities

   Part B

   Which part of the story best helps you know what purpose the author had for writing this selection?

   🍎 the story's title "How a City Grows"

   ★ As the town grew, railroads and factories came—along with even more people looking for jobs.

   ● Now the city is very busy—and very exciting!

COMMON CORE STATE STANDARDS

Informational Text 1. Ask and answer questions about key details in a text. **Informational Text 2.** Identify the main topic and retell key details of a text. **Speaking/Listening 2.** Ask and answer questions about key details in a text read aloud or information presented orally or through other media.

Next

Copyright © Pearson Education, Inc., or its affiliates. All Rights Reserved.

2. Part A

What is one of the last things to happen to a place that becomes a city?

 Millions of people live and work in skyscrapers.

 More people build farms and stores.

 Just a few houses and farms are there.

Part B

Which set of sentences from the selection has the clue word that helps you know what is one of the last things to happen to a place that becomes a city?

 At first there were just a few houses or farms. There were no roads, just trails that deer or other animals followed.

 As more people came, some built their own farms. Others opened small stores.

 Finally, the city was huge! Millions of people lived and worked in tall skyscrapers.

Copyright © Pearson Education, Inc., or its affiliates. All Rights Reserved.

COMMON CORE STATE STANDARDS

Informational Text 1. Ask and answer questions about key details in a text. **Informational Text 2.** Identify the main topic and retell key details of a text. **Speaking/Listening 2.** Ask and answer questions about key details in a text read aloud or information presented orally or through other media.

Next

Name _____

Vocabulary

Directions: Read aloud each question below and have children choose the best answer.

3. Part A

"Long ago, where there's a big city now, there were once just meadows, and hills, and forests." What word from the story means the opposite of "big"?

🍎 more

⭐ small

⬤ huge

Part B

Which detail from the selection can help you identify the word with the opposite meaning of "big"?

🍎 As the town grew, railroads and factories came—along with even more people looking for jobs.

⭐ Like a person, a city starts out small—and grows. At first there were just a few houses or farms.

⬤ Finally, the city was huge! Millions of people lived and worked in tall skyscrapers.

COMMON CORE STATE STANDARDS

Informational Text 4. Ask and answer questions to help determine or clarify the meaning of words and phrases in a text. **Language 4.a.** Use sentence-level context as a clue to the meaning of a word or phrase. **Language 5.** With guidance and support from adults, demonstrate understanding of word relationships and nuances in word meanings.

Copyright © Pearson Education, Inc., or its affiliates. All Rights Reserved.

Next

4. Part A

"There are no cities without jobs for people to do to earn money for their families." What does the word "earn" mean in the selection?

🍎 to be worthy of

⭐ to be rewarded

⚫ to be paid for work

Part B

Which two words from the following sentence best help you know what the word "earn" means?

"There are no cities without jobs for people to do to earn money for their families."

🍎 jobs, money

⭐ cities, money

⚫ jobs, families

Copyright © Pearson Education, Inc., or its affiliates. All Rights Reserved.

COMMON CORE STATE STANDARDS

Informational Text 4. Ask and answer questions to help determine or clarify the meaning of words and phrases in a text. **Language 4.** Determine or clarify the meaning of unknown and multiple-meaning words and phrases based on *grade 1 reading and content,* choosing flexibly from an array of strategies. **Language 4.a.** Use sentence-level context as a clue to the meaning of a word or phrase.

Next

Name _____

Writing — Constructed Response

The selection is about a community growing. Summarize the events that took place. Complete the sentences to put the events in the order that they happened. Use details from the selection.

Long ago, there were just _____.

People came, and at first there were just _____.

More people came and built _____.

The town grew and _____.

Finally, millions _____.

To the Teacher: Use the Writing Rubric on page T19 to assess children's writing.

Copyright © Pearson Education, Inc., or its affiliates. All Rights Reserved.

COMMON CORE STATE STANDARDS

Informational Text 1. Ask and answer questions about key details in a text. **Informational Text 2.** Identify the main topic and retell key details of a text. **Writing 2.** Write informative/explanatory texts in which they name a topic, supply some facts about the topic, and provide some sense of closure.

Next

Writing — Extended Response

You have listened to or read two stories about communities.

- "How a City Grows"
- *Who Works Here?*

Think about the growing town when railroads came in "How a City Grows." Choose one of the workers from *Who Works Here?* What could the worker do in the growing town? Why would the worker be needed there? Write sentences that answer the questions. Use information from the selections in your sentences.

Copyright © Pearson Education, Inc., or its affiliates. All Rights Reserved.

To the Teacher: Tell children they may use the space on this page to plan their writing. Then have them write their response on the following pages. Use the Writing Rubric on page T20 to assess children's writing.

COMMON CORE STATE STANDARDS

Informational Text 1. Ask and answer questions about key details in a text. **Informational Text 2.** Identify the main topic and retell key details of a text. **Writing 2.** Write informative/explanatory texts in which they name a topic, supply some facts about the topic, and provide some sense of closure.

Next

Name _____

_____

- -

_____

- -

_____

- -

_____

- -

_____

- -

_____

- -

_____

- -

_____

- -

_____

- -

_____

- -

_____

Copyright © Pearson Education, Inc., or its affiliates. All Rights Reserved.

Copyright © Pearson Education, Inc., or its affiliates. All Rights Reserved.

Stop

**Directions: Read aloud the following passage to children.
Then read aloud each test item.**

A Clever Trick

One day a mother quail was hunting for insects to eat. Suddenly, she heard a noise. It was just a twig breaking, but it was enough to make her look up and see a fox twenty feet away. Immediately, the quail knew she had to protect her chicks from this enemy.

First, she spread her wings, flew high into the air, and settled in the middle of the path between the fox and her baby chicks.

SQUAWK! SQUAWK! SQUAWK!

Next, the quail pretended she was hurt. She began to hobble about. The fox thought the quail might make a good meal. Since she was injured, he knew that he could easily catch her. The fox didn't know that the quail was only tricking him into thinking she was hurt. He didn't know that she wanted him to chase her so that he would not see the little chicks. It was a good trick to protect her chicks. The quail hobbled down the trail, faster and faster. The fox ran after her, but the bird was always just a little faster.

Copyright © Pearson Education, Inc., or its affiliates. All Rights Reserved.

Next

Last, when the quail was sure she had led the fox far away from her chicks, she flew up into the trees and disappeared. The hungry fox looked at the sky, wondering where the quail had gone.

Copyright © Pearson Education, Inc., or its affiliates. All Rights Reserved.

Next

Text-Based Comprehension

Directions: Read aloud each question below and have children choose the best answer.

I. Part A

The story title is "A Clever Trick." Who does the clever trick?

🍎 the quail

★ the fox

● the chicks

Part B

What detail from the passage helps you know who does the clever trick?

🍎 The fox thought the quail might make a good meal.

★ The fox didn't know that the quail was only tricking him into thinking she was hurt.

● One day a mother quail was hunting for insects to eat.

COMMON CORE STATE STANDARDS

Literature 1. Ask and answer questions about key details in a text. **Literature 3.** Describe characters, settings, and major events in a story, using key details. **Speaking/Listening 2.** Ask and answer questions about key details in a text read aloud or information presented orally or through other media.

Copyright © Pearson Education, Inc. or its affiliates. All Rights Reserved.

Next

2. Part A

What happens before the quail gets between the fox and the quail's chicks?

 The quail flies up into the trees and disappears.

 The quail hears a noise and spots the fox.

 The quail leads the fox away from her chicks.

Part B

Which detail from the story helps you know what happens before the quail gets between the fox and the quail's chicks?

 It was just a twig breaking, but it was enough to make her look up and see a fox twenty feet away.

 He didn't know that she wanted him to chase her so that he would not see the little chicks.

 The hungry fox looked at the sky, wondering where the quail had gone.

Copyright © Pearson Education, Inc., or its affiliates. All Rights Reserved.

COMMON CORE STATE STANDARDS

Literature 1. Ask and answer questions about key details in a text. **Literature 3.** Describe characters, settings, and major events in a story, using key details. **Speaking/Listening 2.** Ask and answer questions about key details in a text read aloud or information presented orally or through other media.

Next

Vocabulary

Directions: Read aloud each question below and have children choose the best answer.

3. **Part A**

"First, she spread her wings, flew high into the air, and settled in the middle of the path between the fox and her baby chicks." What does the word "spread" mean in the passage?

 scattered

 covered

 stretched out

Part B

Which words from the following sentence best help you know what the word "spread" means?

"First, she spread her wings, flew high into the air, and settled in the middle of the path between the fox and her baby chicks."

 high, settled

 wings, flew

 middle, chicks

Copyright © Pearson Education, Inc., or its affiliates. All Rights Reserved.

COMMON CORE STATE STANDARDS

Language 4. Determine or clarify the meaning of unknown and multiple-meaning words and phrases based on *grade 1 reading and content,* choosing flexibly from an array of strategies. **Language 4.a.** Use sentence-level context as a clue to the meaning of a word or phrase.

Next

4. Part A

"He didn't know that she wanted him to chase her so that he would not see the little chicks." What is the meaning of the word "chase" in the sentence?

🍎 follow after to catch

⭐ drive away from

⬤ show the way

Part B

Which sentence from the selection helps you understand the meaning of the word "chase"?

🍎 Immediately, the quail knew she had to protect her chicks from this enemy.

⭐ The fox ran after her, but the bird was always just a little faster.

⬤ The hungry fox looked at the sky, wondering where the quail had gone.

Copyright © Pearson Education, Inc., or its affiliates. All Rights Reserved.

COMMON CORE STATE STANDARDS

Language 4. Determine or clarify the meaning of unknown and multiple-meaning words and phrases based on *grade 1 reading and content,* choosing flexibly from an array of strategies. **Language 4.a.** Use sentence-level context as a clue to the meaning of a word or phrase.

Next

Name _____

Writing – Constructed Response

How is the mother quail a good parent to her chicks? Write some sentences telling what the mother quail does that makes her a good parent. Use information from the passage in your sentences.

_____

_____

_____

_____

_____

_____

_____

_____

_____

_____

Copyright © Pearson Education, Inc., or its affiliates. All Rights Reserved.

To the Teacher: Use the Writing Rubric on page T19 to assess children's writing.

COMMON CORE STATE STANDARDS

Literature 1. Ask and answer questions about key details in a text. **Literature 3.** Describe characters, settings, and major events in a story, using key details. **Writing 2.** Write informative/explanatory texts in which they name a topic, supply some facts about the topic, and provide some sense of closure.

Next

Writing — Extended Response

You have listened to or read two selections about animals.

- "A Clever Trick"
- *The Big Circle*

Both "A Clever Trick" and *The Big Circle* tell about animals protecting their young. What does the mother quail protect her chicks from? How does she protect them? What do the triceratops protect their young from? How do they protect their young? Write sentences that compare and contrast the ways the animals protect their young. Use information from the selections in your sentences.

Copyright © Pearson Education, Inc., or its affiliates. All Rights Reserved.

To the Teacher: Tell children they may use the space on this page to plan their writing. Then have them write their response on the following pages. Use the Writing Rubric on page T20 to assess children's writing.

COMMON CORE STATE STANDARDS

Literature 1. Ask and answer questions about key details in a text. **Literature 3.** Describe characters, settings, and major events in a story, using key details. **Literature 9.** Compare and contrast the adventures and experiences of characters in stories. **Writing 2.** Write informative/explanatory texts in which they name a topic, supply some facts about the topic, and provide some sense of closure.

Next

Name _____

Copyright © Pearson Education, Inc., or its affiliates. All Rights Reserved.

Next

Copyright © Pearson Education, Inc., or its affiliates. All Rights Reserved.

Name _____

**Directions: Read aloud the following passage to children.
Then read aloud each test item.**

Life in the Forest
by Claire Daniel

We can find life in the forest. It is a busy place!

Sun helped the leaves get wide and flat.

Sun shines on the leaves and helps them grow.
Bugs like munching on them. Yum, yum! Bugs can eat
lots and lots.

The woodpecker sits on a branch. Peck! Peck! Peck! It
pecks to get at bugs.

The holes tell us that woodpeckers pecked on the tree.

The huge log is soft and damp. Water has made the
log rot. Small bugs made homes in the log.

The bird hops on the log and then pecks at it. Yum,
yum! It gets bugs when it pecks.

Nuts grow on trees and then fall all around. Squirrels
get nuts and munch on them. Yum, yum!

A fox is cute, but it likes to catch small animals.

Copyright © Pearson Education, Inc., or its affiliates. All Rights Reserved.

Next

The black bear eats grass, nuts, and grubs. Grubs are small bugs that hide under rocks and logs.

The bear picked up the rocks and hunted for grubs.

Many plants have shapes like tubes. Small hummingbirds can sip from the plants.

The hummingbird uses its bill to get food. It sticks its bill in the plant. Hummingbirds can catch small bugs too.

The big forest is filled with life. Many animals and plants call it home. It is a busy place!

Copyright © Pearson Education, Inc., or its affiliates. All Rights Reserved.

Next

Name _____

Text-Based Comprehension

Directions: Read aloud each question below and have children choose the best answer.

I. Part A

What is the author's purpose for writing this selection?

🍎 to entertain readers with a story about animals

⭐ to give an opinion about a forest

⬤ to provide information about life in the forest

Part B

Which sentences from the story help you know what purpose the author had for writing this selection?

🍎 The woodpecker sits on a branch. Peck! Peck! Peck! It pecks to get at bugs.

⭐ The big forest is filled with life. Many animals and plants call it home. It is a busy place!

⬤ The black bear eats grass, nuts, and grubs. Grubs are small bugs that hide under rocks and logs.

COMMON CORE STATE STANDARDS

Informational Text 1. Ask and answer questions about key details in a text. **Informational Text 8.** Identify the reasons an author gives to support points in a text. **Speaking/Listening 2.** Ask and answer questions about key details in a text read aloud or information presented orally or through other media.

Copyright © Pearson Education, Inc., or its affiliates. All Rights Reserved.

Next

2. **Part A**

Which sentence from the selection tells that animals live in the forest?

 Nuts grow on trees and then fall all around.

 Many plants have shapes like tubes.

 Many animals and plants call it home.

Part B

What kinds of animals live in the forest?

 birds, squirrels, foxes, bears

 trees, plants, leaves, nuts

 bugs, logs, rocks, grubs

Copyright © Pearson Education, Inc., or its affiliates. All Rights Reserved.

COMMON CORE STATE STANDARDS

Informational Text 1. Ask and answer questions about key details in a text. **Informational Text 7.** Use the illustrations and details in a text to describe its key ideas. **Speaking/Listening 2.** Ask and answer questions about key details in a text read aloud or information presented orally or through other media.

Next

Name _____

Vocabulary

Directions: Read aloud each question below and have children choose the best answer.

3. Part A

The selection says, "The woodpecker sits on a branch. Peck! Peck! Peck! It pecks to get at bugs." Which word is a sound word?

 get

 peck

 bugs

Part B

What makes this sound?

 woodpecker

 bugs

 branch

Copyright © Pearson Education, Inc., or its affiliates. All Rights Reserved.

COMMON CORE STATE STANDARDS

Informational Text 4. Ask and answer questions to help determine or clarify the meaning of words and phrases in a text. **Language 4.** Determine or clarify the meaning of unknown and multiple-meaning words and phrases based on *grade 1 reading and content,* choosing flexibly from an array of strategies. **Language 4.a.** Use sentence-level context as a clue to the meaning of a word or phrase.

Next

4. Part A

The selection says, "The black bear eats grass, nuts, and grubs." What does the word "grubs" mean?

🍎 bear

⭐ eats

● bugs

Part B

Which detail from the story helps you understand the meaning of the word "grubs"?

🍎 The bear picked up the rocks and hunted for grubs.

⭐ Grubs are small bugs that hide under rocks and logs.

● Yum, yum! It gets bugs when it pecks.

Copyright © Pearson Education, Inc., or its affiliates. All Rights Reserved.

COMMON CORE STATE STANDARDS

Informational Text 4. Ask and answer questions to help determine or clarify the meaning of words and phrases in a text. **Language 4.** Determine or clarify the meaning of unknown and multiple-meaning words and phrases based on *grade 1 reading and content,* choosing flexibly from an array of strategies. **Language 4.a.** Use sentence-level context as a clue to the meaning of a word or phrase.

Next

Name _____

Writing — Constructed Response

In the selection *Life in the Forest,* we learn about many animals. Choose an animal. Write sentences telling about the animal. Use information from the selection in your sentences.

_____

_____

_____

_____

_____

_____

_____

_____

_____

Copyright © Pearson Education, Inc., or its affiliates. All Rights Reserved.

To the Teacher: Use the Writing Rubric on page T19 to assess children's writing.

COMMON CORE STATE STANDARDS

Informational Text 1. Ask and answer questions about key details in a text. **Writing 2.** Write informative/explanatory texts in which they name a topic, supply some facts about the topic, and provide some sense of closure. **Writing 8.** With guidance and support from adults, recall information from experiences or gather information from provided sources to answer a question.

Next

Writing — Extended Response

You have listened to or read two selections about animals.

- *Life in the Forest*
- "A Clever Trick"

Both *Life in the Forest* and "A Clever Trick" are about animals. Compare the make-believe animal in "A Clever Trick" with one of the real animals in *Life in the Forest*. Tell how the animals are alike and how they are different. Use information from the selections in your sentences.

Copyright © Pearson Education, Inc., or its affiliates. All Rights Reserved.

To the Teacher: Tell children they may use the space on this page to plan their writing. Then have them write their response on the following pages. Use the Writing Rubric on page T20 to assess children's writing.

COMMON CORE STATE STANDARDS

Informational Text 1. Ask and answer questions about key details in a text. **Writing 2.** Write informative/explanatory texts in which they name a topic, supply some facts about the topic, and provide some sense of closure. **Writing 8.** With guidance and support from adults, recall information from experiences or gather information from provided sources to answer a question.

Next

Name _____

Copyright © Pearson Education, Inc., or its affiliates. All Rights Reserved.

Copyright © Pearson Education, Inc., or its affiliates. All Rights Reserved.

Name _____

**Directions: Read aloud the following passage to children.
Then read aloud each test item.**

Honey Bees

by Jesús Cervantes

The sun shines. The honey bees wake up. It is time for the insects to work. Buzz, buzz, buzz.

In the hive, bees live like a family. In the hive there is a queen bee, lots of worker bees, and some drones.

One is the queen bee. She rules the hive.

Some bees are drones. Drones help the queen bee.

The hive is hidden in a big tree. Worker bees will keep the hive safe.

It is not wise to make bees mad! Mad bees will attack.

Worker bees make wax cells in the hive. The wax cells are small holes. Bees save honey in some wax cells. Small bees live and grow big in other cells.

Bees feed on honey. Worker bees feed honey to other bees in the hive. Bees make honey from nectar.

Bees get nectar inside flowers. Bees take the sweet nectar back home.

Copyright © Pearson Education, Inc., or its affiliates. All Rights Reserved.

Next

Bees also get pollen from flowers. Worker bees feed pollen to the queen bee and small bees. It helps them get big. When those small bees get big, it is time to make a new hive.

Worker bees make the new hive. A new queen bee will go with them.

When it gets cold, the bees will go inside their hive and sleep and rest. The bees will wake up when the sun shines.

Copyright © Pearson Education, Inc., or its affiliates. All Rights Reserved.

Name _____

Text-Based Comprehension

Directions: Read aloud each question below and have children choose the best answer.

1. Part A

What is the main idea of the selection?

 The selection tells about big trees.

 The selection tells about honey bees.

 The selection tells about the sun shining.

Part B

Which sentences from the selection help you identify the main idea?

 Bees get nectar inside flowers. Bees take the sweet nectar back home.

 The hive is hidden in a big tree. Worker bees will keep the hive safe.

 The honey bees wake up. It is time for the insects to work.

Copyright © Pearson Education, Inc., or its affiliates. All Rights Reserved.

COMMON CORE STATE STANDARDS

Informational Text 1. Ask and answer questions about key details in a text. **Informational Text 2.** Identify the main topic and retell key details of a text. **Informational Text 3.** Describe the connection between two individuals, events, ideas, or pieces of information in a text. **Speaking/Listening 2.** Ask and answer questions about key details in a text read aloud or information presented orally or through other media.

Next

2. Part A

What kinds of honey bees live in the hive?

 queen bee, worker bees, wax bees

 queen bee, worker bees, drones

 queen bee, drones, king bee

Part B

Which detail from the story helps you know what kinds of honey bees live in the hive?

 there is a queen bee, lots of worker bees, and some drones

 Worker bees feed honey to other bees in the hive.

 Worker bees feed pollen to the queen bee and small bees.

Copyright © Pearson Education, Inc., or its affiliates. All Rights Reserved.

COMMON CORE STATE STANDARDS

Informational Text 1. Ask and answer questions about key details in a text. **Informational Text 3.** Describe the connection between two individuals, events, ideas, or pieces of information in a text. **Speaking/Listening 2.** Ask and answer questions about key details in a text read aloud or information presented orally or through other media.

Next

Name _____

Vocabulary

Directions: Read aloud each question below and have children choose the best answer.

3. Part A

The selection says, "One is the queen bee. She rules the hive." What does the word "rules" mean in this sentence?

🍎 someone who knows what to do

⭐ someone who is in charge

⬤ someone who is not in charge

Part B

Which detail from the selection best helps you know what the word "rules" means?

🍎 The queen and other bees live in the hive.

⭐ Bees sleep and rest when it gets cold.

⬤ Other bees help and feed the queen.

Copyright © Pearson Education, Inc., or its affiliates. All Rights Reserved.

COMMON CORE STATE STANDARDS

Language 4. Determine or clarify the meaning of unknown and multiple-meaning words and phrases based on *grade 1 reading and content,* choosing flexibly from an array of strategies. **Language 4.a.** Use sentence-level context as a clue to the meaning of a word or phrase. **Language 5.** With guidance and support from adults, demonstrate understanding of word relationships and nuances in word meanings.

Next

4. Part A

The selection says, "When those small bees get big, it is time to make a new hive." Which two words are opposite in meaning?

🍎 it, time

⭐ small, big

⬤ get, make

Part B

Which word in the following sentence gives a clue that the two words are opposite?

"When those small bees get big, it is time to make a new hive."

🍎 is

⭐ to

⬤ get

Copyright © Pearson Education, Inc., or its affiliates. All Rights Reserved.

COMMON CORE STATE STANDARDS

Language 4. Determine or clarify the meaning of unknown and multiple-meaning words and phrases based on *grade 1 reading and content,* choosing flexibly from an array of strategies. **Language 4.a.** Use sentence-level context as a clue to the meaning of a word or phrase.

Next

Writing — Constructed Response

In the selection *Honey Bees,* we learn about honey bees. Draw a picture of a bee doing something you learned from the selection. Write sentences for your picture to tell something you learned about bees. Use information from the selection in your sentences.

Copyright © Pearson Education, Inc., or its affiliates. All Rights Reserved.

_____

_____

_____

_____

To the Teacher: Use the Writing Rubric on page T19 to assess children's writing.

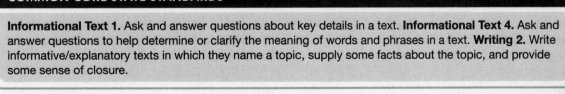

COMMON CORE STATE STANDARDS

Informational Text 1. Ask and answer questions about key details in a text. **Informational Text 4.** Ask and answer questions to help determine or clarify the meaning of words and phrases in a text. **Writing 2.** Write informative/explanatory texts in which they name a topic, supply some facts about the topic, and provide some sense of closure.

Next

Writing — Extended Response

You have listened to selections about animals.

- *Life in the Forest*
- *Honey Bees*

Both the selections tell where animals live and what they do. Choose an animal and write sentences to tell something you learned about the animal. Use information from the selections in your sentences.

Copyright © Pearson Education, Inc., or its affiliates. All Rights Reserved.

To the Teacher: Tell children they may use the space on this page to plan their writing. Then have them write their response on the following pages. Use the Writing Rubric on page T20 to assess children's writing.

COMMON CORE STATE STANDARDS

Informational Text 1. Ask and answer questions about key details in a text. **Informational Text 4.** Ask and answer questions to help determine or clarify the meaning of words and phrases in a text. **Writing 2.** Write informative/explanatory texts in which they name a topic, supply some facts about the topic, and provide some sense of closure.

Next

Name _____

Copyright © Pearson Education, Inc., or its affiliates. All Rights Reserved.

Next

Copyright © Pearson Education, Inc., or its affiliates. All Rights Reserved.

Stop

Directions: Read the following passage. Use information from the passage to answer the questions.

A Place to Play
by Cynthia Chin-Lee

Benny and Molly go to see their new neighborhood center with their grandmother Nai Nai.

"This will be a fun day," Benny said to Molly. "Nai Nai can take us to see where Mom and Dad are working."

"I spy Dad and Mom!" said Benny. "What are you doing?"

"We are planting things. This sunny spot is good for growing plants," said Dad.

"It is muddy in that spot!" said Benny. "Let us go inside," said Nai Nai.

"Here is a place for meetings," said Mom. "Look, Benny! There is Ms. Torres!"

"Hi, Benny!" said Ms. Torres. "I grew up in this neighborhood, so I want to help."

"This is a place for art," said Mom. "Look at the wall with nothing on it. Now look at the wall next to it."

Copyright © Pearson Education, Inc., or its affiliates. All Rights Reserved.

Next

"That wall looks like my neighborhood!" said Benny.
"I see people working and playing under a blue sky."

"Do you like it?" asked Mr. Gray. Benny said, "Yes,
I hope it stays there always!"

"This will become a place to watch plays," said Dad.

"Look, there is Mr. Jackson," said Mom. "He lives by
us too."

"People from the neighborhood came together to work
on everything in this place," Mom said.

Benny saw a boy who seemed a little shy. "Do you like
to play ball?" Benny asked.

"Go check out this next one," said Dad.

"I will slide down!" Benny said. Mom and Molly went up
in the tower.

"They are lucky," said Nai Nai. "I wish I had a place like
this when I was a kid."

"See the sunset?" Mom asked.

Dad said, "It is time to go home."

"I like this place," said Benny. "It is a good place for
all of us!"

Copyright © Pearson Education, Inc., or its affiliates. All Rights Reserved.

Next

Name _____

Text-Based Comprehension

Directions: Read the questions below and choose the best answer.

I. Part A

What kind of work are Mom and Dad doing at the place in the story?

○ **A.** putting art on the walls

○ **B.** making money for the family

○ **C.** making the garden nice

○ **D.** building a playground

Part B

Which sentence from the story best helps you know what kind of work Mom and Dad are doing?

○ **A.** "This is a place for art," said Mom.

○ **B.** "Nai Nai can take us to see where Mom and Dad are working."

○ **C.** "We are planting things."

○ **D.** "People from the neighborhood came together to work on everything in this place," Mom said.

Copyright © Pearson Education, Inc., or its affiliates. All Rights Reserved.

COMMON CORE STATE STANDARDS

Literature 1. Ask and answer questions about key details in a text. **Literature 3.** Describe characters, settings, and major events in a story, using key details.

Next

2. Part A

What does Molly do last?

○ **A.** goes up in a tower

○ **B.** looks at a place for art

○ **C.** plays ball

○ **D.** looks at a meeting place

Part B

Which detail in the story helps you know what Molly does last?

○ **A.** "This will be a fun day," Benny said to Molly.

○ **B.** "Do you like to play ball?" Benny asked.

○ **C.** "I spy Dad and Mom!" said Benny.

○ **D.** Dad said, "It is time to go home."

Copyright © Pearson Education, Inc., or its affiliates. All Rights Reserved.

COMMON CORE STATE STANDARDS

Literature 1. Ask and answer questions about key details in a text. **Literature 3.** Describe characters, settings, and major events in a story, using key details.

Next

Name _____

Vocabulary

Directions: Read the questions below and choose the best answer.

3. Part A

Mom says, "Look at the wall with nothing on it. Now look at the wall next to it." What is the opposite of "nothing" in the first sentence?

○ **A.** something

○ **B.** blank

○ **C.** other

○ **D.** never

Part B

Which sentence from the story most helps you know which word was the opposite for the word "nothing"?

○ **A.** "I see people working and playing under a blue sky."

○ **B.** "Here is a place for meetings," said Mom.

○ **C.** "Do you like to play ball?" Benny asked.

○ **D.** Mom and Molly went up in the tower.

Copyright © Pearson Education, Inc., or its affiliates. All Rights Reserved.

COMMON CORE STATE STANDARDS

Literature 4. Identify words and phrases in stories or poems that suggest feelings or appeal to the senses.
Language 4.a. Use sentence-level context as a clue to the meaning of a word or phrase.

Next

4. Part A

What does Mom mean by the word "sunset" at the end of the story?

○ **A.** The day is beginning.

○ **B.** The day is bright.

○ **C.** The day is cloudy.

○ **D.** The day is ending.

Part B

Which sentence in the passage helps you understand the meaning of "sunset"?

○ **A.** "This will be a fun day," Benny said to Molly.

○ **B.** Dad said, "It is time to go home."

○ **C.** "It is muddy in that spot!" said Benny.

○ **D.** "This sunny spot is good for growing plants," said Dad.

Copyright © Pearson Education, Inc., or its affiliates. All Rights Reserved.

COMMON CORE STATE STANDARDS

Literature 4. Identify words and phrases in stories or poems that suggest feelings or appeal to the senses.
Language 4.a. Use sentence-level context as a clue to the meaning of a word or phrase.

Next

Name _____

Writing – Constructed Response

What place in your neighborhood is like the one in the story? Tell about the place. Tell how it is like the place where Benny and Molly go.

_____

- -

_____

- -

_____

- -

_____

- -

_____

- -

_____

- -

_____

- -

_____

Copyright © Pearson Education, Inc., or its affiliates. All Rights Reserved.

To the Teacher: Use the Writing Rubric on page T19 to assess children's writing.

COMMON CORE STATE STANDARDS

Literature 1. Ask and answer questions about key details in a text. **Writing 2.** Write informative/explanatory texts in which they name a topic, supply some facts about the topic, and provide some sense of closure. **Writing 8.** With guidance and support from adults, recall information from experiences or gather information from provided sources to answer a question.

Next

Writing — Extended Response

You have read two stories about neighborhoods.

- "A Place to Play"
- "My Neighborhood, Then and Now"

Imagine a new place in your neighborhood. What would the place have? What could people do together there? Use details from "A Place to Play" and "My Neighborhood, Then and Now" as examples in your writing. Check your writing for correct capitalization, punctuation, and spelling.

Copyright © Pearson Education, Inc., or its affiliates. All Rights Reserved.

To the Teacher: Tell children they may use the space on this page to plan their writing. Then have them write their response on the following pages. Use the Writing Rubric on page T20 to assess children's writing.

COMMON CORE STATE STANDARDS

Literature 1. Ask and answer questions about key details in a text. **Writing 3.** Write narratives in which they recount two or more appropriately sequenced events, include some details regarding what happened, use temporal words to signal event order, and provide some sense of closure. **Writing 8.** With guidance and support from adults, recall information from experiences or gather information from provided sources to answer a question. **Language 2.** Demonstrate command of the conventions of standard English capitalization, punctuation, and spelling when writing.

Next

Name _____

_____
- -
_____
- -
_____
- -
_____
- -
_____
- -
_____
- -
_____
- -
_____
- -
_____
- -
_____
- -

Copyright © Pearson Education, Inc., or its affiliates. All Rights Reserved.

Next

Copyright © Pearson Education, Inc., or its affiliates. All Rights Reserved.

Name _____

Directions: Read the following passage. Use information from the passage to answer the questions.

Ruby in Her Own Time

by Jonathan Emmett

Once upon a time upon a nest beside a lake, there lived two ducks—a mother duck and a father duck.

There were five eggs in the nest. Mother Duck sat upon the nest, all day and all night . . . through howling wind and driving rain, looking after the eggs—all five of them.

Then, one bright morning, the eggs began to hatch. One, two, three, four little beaks poked out into the sunlight.

One, two, three, four little ducklings shook their feathers in the breeze. "We'll call them Rufus, Rory, Rosie, and Rebecca," said Father Duck. And Mother Duck agreed.

But the fifth egg did nothing. "Will it ever hatch?" said Father Duck. "It will," said Mother Duck, "in its own time."

And—sure enough—it did. "She's very small," said Father Duck. "What shall we call her?" "We'll call her Ruby," said Mother Duck, "because she's small and precious." . . .

Copyright © Pearson Education, Inc., or its affiliates. All Rights Reserved.

Next

Rufus, Rory, Rosie, and Rebecca swam off whenever they were able. They swam anywhere and everywhere.

But Ruby swam nowhere. "Will she ever swim?" said Father Duck. "She will," said Mother Duck, "in her own time." And—sure enough—she did.

Rufus, Rory, Rosie, and Rebecca grew bigger. And Ruby grew bigger too. Her feathers grew out, and her wings grew broad and beautiful.

And when Rufus, Rory, Rosie, and Rebecca began to fly . . . Ruby flew too!

Rufus, Rory, Rosie, and Rebecca flew far and wide. They flew out across the water. They flew up among the trees.

But Ruby flew farther and wider. She flew out beyond the water. She flew up above the trees.

She flew anywhere and everywhere. She stretched out her beautiful wings and soared high among the clouds.

Mother Duck and Father Duck watched Ruby flying off into the distance.

"Will she ever come back?" said Mother Duck. "She will," said Father Duck, "in her own time."

And—sure enough—she did.

Copyright © Pearson Education, Inc., or its affiliates. All Rights Reserved.

Next

Name _____

Text-Based Comprehension

Directions: Read the questions below and choose the best answer.

I. Part A

What is the main way Ruby is different from her brothers and sisters?

○ **A.** Her wings are not beautiful.

○ **B.** She does not learn to swim.

○ **C.** She stays home with her parents.

○ **D.** She does things later than they do.

Part B

Which detail from the story best helps you know that Ruby is different from her brothers and sisters?

○ **A.** …Ruby flew too!

○ **B.** "She will," said Mother Duck, "in her own time."

○ **C.** And Ruby grew bigger too.

○ **D.** her wings grew broad and beautiful

Copyright © Pearson Education, Inc., or its affiliates. All Rights Reserved.

COMMON CORE STATE STANDARDS

Literature 1. Ask and answer questions about key details in a text. **Literature 3.** Describe characters, settings, and major events in a story, using key details.

Next

2. Part A

What main lesson does the story teach?

○ **A.** It is easy for ducks to learn to swim.

○ **B.** Ducks have many brothers and sisters.

○ **C.** Everyone grows and learns differently.

○ **D.** Ducks do not like to leave their homes.

Part B

Which detail from the passage helps you know the main lesson of the story?

○ **A.** One, two, three, four little ducklings shook their feathers in the breeze.

○ **B.** Mother Duck and Father Duck watched Ruby flying off into the distance.

○ **C.** But Ruby swam nowhere.

○ **D.** "She will," said Mother Duck, "in her own time."

Copyright © Pearson Education, Inc., or its affiliates. All Rights Reserved.

COMMON CORE STATE STANDARDS

Literature 1. Ask and answer questions about key details in a text. **Language 2.** Retell stories, including key details, and demonstrate understanding of their central message or lesson.

Next

Name _____

Vocabulary

Directions: Read the questions below and choose the best answer.

3. **Part A**

Which word means about the same as "howling" in the following sentence?

"Mother Duck sat upon the nest, all day and all night . . . through howling wind and driving rain, looking after the eggs—all five of them."

- ○ **A.** soft
- ○ **B.** noisy
- ○ **C.** morning
- ○ **D.** quiet

Part B

Which detail from the sentence most helps you know what "howling" means in the story?

"Mother Duck sat upon the nest, all day and all night . . . through howling wind and driving rain, looking after the eggs—all five of them."

- ○ **A.** looking after the eggs
- ○ **B.** sat upon the nest
- ○ **C.** all day and all night
- ○ **D.** driving rain

COMMON CORE STATE STANDARDS

Literature 4. Identify words and phrases in stories or poems that suggest feelings or appeal to the senses.
Language 4.a. Use sentence-level context as a clue to the meaning of a word or phrase.

Copyright © Pearson Education, Inc., or its affiliates. All Rights Reserved.

Next

4. Part A

Which word means the opposite of "everywhere" in the following sentence?

"They swam anywhere and everywhere."

○ **A.** beyond

○ **B.** nowhere

○ **C.** anywhere

○ **D.** whenever

Part B

Which detail from the story best helps you figure out the opposite of "everywhere"?

○ **A.** But Ruby swam nowhere.

○ **B.** She flew out beyond the water.

○ **C.** They flew up among the trees.

○ **D.** Rufus, Rory . . . swam off whenever they were able.

Copyright © Pearson Education, Inc., or its affiliates. All Rights Reserved.

COMMON CORE STATE STANDARDS

Literature 4. Identify words and phrases in stories or poems that suggest feelings or appeal to the senses.
Language 4.a. Use sentence-level context as a clue to the meaning of a word or phrase.

Next

Name _____

Writing – Constructed Response

How are you like Ruby? Tell about something you did in your own time. Tell how you felt after you did it.

_____

- -

_____

- -

_____

- -

_____

- -

_____

- -

_____

- -

_____

Copyright © Pearson Education, Inc., or its affiliates. All Rights Reserved.

To the Teacher: Use the Writing Rubric on page T19 to assess children's writing.

COMMON CORE STATE STANDARDS

Literature 7. Use illustrations and details in a story to describe its characters, setting, or events.
Writing 3. Write narratives in which they recount two or more appropriately sequenced events, include some details regarding what happened, use temporal words to signal event order, and provide some sense of closure. **Writing 8.** With guidance and support from adults, recall information from experiences or gather information from provided sources to answer a question.

Next

Writing — Extended Response

You have read two stories about baby birds.

- *Ruby in Her Own Time*
- "The Ugly Duckling"

Which of the two stories did you like better? Why did you like this story better? Did you like its main character better than the main character of the other story? What would you tell another reader about the story? Write sentences to tell why you liked one story better than the other. Name the stories in your sentences. In your last sentence, tell why another reader should read the story. Check your writing for correct capitalization, punctuation, and spelling.

Copyright © Pearson Education, Inc., or its affiliates. All Rights Reserved.

To the Teacher: Tell children they may use the space on this page to plan their writing. Then have them write their response on the following pages. Use the Writing Rubric on page T20 to assess children's writing.

COMMON CORE STATE STANDARDS

Writing 1. Write opinion pieces in which they introduce the topic or name the book they are writing about, state an opinion, supply a reason for the opinion, and provide some sense of closure. **Writing 8.** With guidance and support from adults, recall information from experiences or gather information from provided sources to answer a question. **Language 1.** Demonstrate command of the conventions of standard English grammar and usage when writing or speaking. **Language 2.** Demonstrate command of the conventions of standard English capitalization, punctuation, and spelling when writing.

Next

Name _____

_____

- -

_____

- -

_____

- -

_____

- -

_____

- -

_____

_____

- -

_____

- -

_____

_____

- -

_____

- -

_____

Copyright © Pearson Education, Inc., or its affiliates. All Rights Reserved.

Next

Copyright © Pearson Education, Inc., or its affiliates. All Rights Reserved.

Name _____

Directions: Read the following passage. Use information from the passage to answer the questions.

The Class Pet
by Nichole L. Shields

Miss Ford takes a glass box to school. "This will be a house for our class pet," Miss Ford tells the class.

The pet is a cute tan mouse. The class names it Dory. Miss Ford teaches lessons on pets. She uses Dory in these lessons.

Dory is tan. But mice can be black, white, or brown. Mice can have stripes or spots too.

Mice need to eat and drink. Pet stores may sell seed mixes or hard pellets. But mice will eat all sorts of things, such as corn and nuts.

Mice like to run and jump late at night. It is time for them to sleep when the sun rises.

Mice use torn cloth and cotton to make nests. Mice that live outside use grass and branches.

A mom can have lots of very small mice. Ten of them can be born at the same time. They nap in a nest. When mice are born, they have no fur. These mice cannot see yet.

Copyright © Pearson Education, Inc., or its affiliates. All Rights Reserved.

Next

For a short time, small mice cannot eat seeds. They just sleep and drink milk. Time passes and small mice get fur.

More time passes and small mice can see. They can be away from the nest. These mice can eat seeds and nuts like their mom.

Miss Ford tells the class that mice like friends. She tells the class that Dory wishes for one.

The next week, Miss Ford takes a box from her car. In it is a mouse. The class names it Cory. Dory and Cory become friends.

Copyright © Pearson Education, Inc., or its affiliates. All Rights Reserved.

Next

Text-Based Comprehension

Directions: Read the questions below and choose the best answer.

1. Part A

Which sentence from the passage is an opinion?

○ **A.** But mice can be black, white, or brown.

○ **B.** The pet is a cute tan mouse.

○ **C.** Mice can have stripes or spots too.

○ **D.** Mice need to eat and drink.

Part B

Which clue word shows that the sentence is an opinion?

○ **A.** too

○ **B.** need

○ **C.** cute

○ **D.** but

Copyright © Pearson Education, Inc., or its affiliates. All Rights Reserved.

COMMON CORE STATE STANDARDS

Informational Text 1. Ask and answer questions about key details in a text.

Next

2. Part A

How are newborn mice different from their mom?

- ◯ **A.** They have more fur.
- ◯ **B.** They see better.
- ◯ **C.** They play more.
- ◯ **D.** They eat different foods.

Part B

Which sentence most helps you know how newborn mice are different from their mom?

- ◯ **A.** Mice need to eat and drink.
- ◯ **B.** Pet stores may sell seed mixes or hard pellets.
- ◯ **C.** For a short time, small mice cannot eat seeds.
- ◯ **D.** Miss Ford tells the class that mice like friends.

Copyright © Pearson Education, Inc., or its affiliates. All Rights Reserved.

COMMON CORE STATE STANDARDS

Informational Text 1. Ask and answer questions about key details in a text. **Informational Text 3.** Describe the connection between two individuals, events, ideas, or pieces of information in a text.

Next

Name _____

Vocabulary

Directions: Read the questions below and choose the best answer.

3. Part A

What word group does the word "tan" belong to?

○ **A.** sizes

○ **B.** patterns

○ **C.** colors

○ **D.** foods

Part B

Which sentence from the passage helps you know what word group "tan" belongs to?

○ **A.** But mice can be black, white, or brown.

○ **B.** Mice can have stripes or spots too.

○ **C.** Mice need to eat and drink.

○ **D.** Pet stores may sell seed mixes or hard pellets.

Copyright © Pearson Education, Inc., or its affiliates. All Rights Reserved.

COMMON CORE STATE STANDARDS

Informational Text 4. Ask and answer questions to help determine or clarify the meaning of words and phrases in a text. **Language 5.a.** Sort words into categories (e.g., colors, clothing) to gain a sense of the concepts the categories represent.

Next

4. Part A

What does the word "pellets" mean in the following sentences from the story?

"Mice need to eat and drink. Pet stores may sell seed mixes or hard pellets."

○ **A.** beds for pets

○ **B.** little rocks

○ **C.** sweet drinks

○ **D.** small round pieces

Part B

"Mice need to eat and drink. Pet stores may sell seed mixes or hard pellets."

Which word in this part of the story most helps you understand the meaning of "pellets" in the passage?

○ **A.** eat

○ **B.** drink

○ **C.** seed

○ **D.** mixes

Copyright © Pearson Education, Inc., or its affiliates. All Rights Reserved.

COMMON CORE STATE STANDARDS

Informational Text 4. Ask and answer questions to help determine or clarify the meaning of words and phrases in a text. **Language 4.** Determine or clarify the meaning of unknown and multiple-meaning words and phrases based on *grade 1 reading and content*, choosing flexibly from an array of strategies. **Language 4.a.** Use sentence-level context as a clue to the meaning of a word or phrase.

Next

Writing — Constructed Response

Suppose your class got a pet mouse. How would you care for it? Use facts and details from the story to help you write.

_____
_____
_____
_____
_____
_____
_____
_____
_____
_____
_____
_____
_____
_____

Copyright © Pearson Education, Inc., or its affiliates. All Rights Reserved.

To the Teacher: Use the Writing Rubric on page T19 to assess children's writing.

COMMON CORE STATE STANDARDS

Informational Text 7. Use the illustrations and details in a text to describe its key ideas. **Writing 2.** Write informative/explanatory texts in which they name a topic, supply some facts about the topic, and provide some sense of closure. **Writing 8.** With guidance and support from adults, recall information from experiences or gather information from provided sources to answer a question.

Writing — Extended Response

You have read two stories about mice.

- *The Class Pet*
- "Belling the Cat"

Suppose you had a pet mouse and a pet cat at home. What problem would you have? How would you solve the problem? Use details from "Belling the Cat" and *The Class Pet* to help you explain your problem and describe how you would solve it. Check your writing for correct capitalization, punctuation, and spelling.

To the Teacher: Tell children they may use the space on this page to plan their writing. Then have them write their response on the following pages. Use the Writing Rubric on page T20 to assess children's writing.

Copyright © Pearson Education, Inc., or its affiliates. All Rights Reserved.

COMMON CORE STATE STANDARDS

Informational Text 3. Describe the connection between two individuals, events, ideas, or pieces of information in a text. **Writing 2.** Write informative/explanatory texts in which they name a topic, supply some facts about the topic, and provide some sense of closure. **Writing 8.** With guidance and support from adults, recall information from experiences or gather information from provided sources to answer a question. **Language 1.** Demonstrate command of the conventions of standard English grammar and usage when writing or speaking. **Language 2.** Demonstrate command of the conventions of standard English capitalization, punctuation, and spelling when writing.

Next

Name _____

Copyright © Pearson Education, Inc., or its affiliates. All Rights Reserved.

Next

Copyright © Pearson Education, Inc., or its affiliates. All Rights Reserved.

Name _____

Directions: Read the following passage. Use information from the passage to answer the questions.

Frog and Toad Together: The Garden (Part 1)

by Arnold Lobel

Frog was in his garden. Toad came walking by.

"What a fine garden you have, Frog," he said.

"Yes," said Frog. "It is very nice, but it was hard work."

"I wish I had a garden," said Toad.

"Here are some flower seeds. Plant them in the ground," said Frog, "and soon you will have a garden."

"How soon?" asked Toad.

"Quite soon," said Frog.

Toad ran home. He planted the flower seeds.

"Now seeds," said Toad, "start growing."

Toad walked up and down a few times. The seeds did not start to grow.

Copyright © Pearson Education, Inc., or its affiliates. All Rights Reserved.

Next

Toad put his head close to the ground and said loudly, **"Now seeds, start growing!"**

Toad looked at the ground again. The seeds did not start to grow.

Toad put his head very close to the ground and shouted, **"NOW SEEDS, START GROWING!"**

Frog came running up the path. "What is all this noise?" he asked.

"My seeds will not grow," said Toad.

"You are shouting too much," said Frog. "These poor seeds are afraid to grow."

"My seeds are afraid to grow?" asked Toad.

"Of course," said Frog. "Leave them alone for a few days. Let the sun shine on them, let the rain fall on them. Soon your seeds will start to grow."

Copyright © Pearson Education, Inc., or its affiliates. All Rights Reserved.

Next

Name _____

Text-Based Comprehension

Directions: Read the questions below and choose the best answer.

I. **Part A**

Why does Toad want a garden?

○ **A.** because he likes digging in dirt

○ **B.** because he wants food to eat

○ **C.** because he sees Frog's garden

○ **D.** because he likes flowers

Part B

Which sentence from the story best helps you understand why Toad wants a garden?

○ **A.** "I wish I had a garden," said Toad.

○ **B.** He planted the flower seeds.

○ **C.** The seeds did not start to grow.

○ **D.** "What a fine garden you have, Frog," he said.

Copyright © Pearson Education, Inc., or its affiliates. All Rights Reserved.

COMMON CORE STATE STANDARDS

Literature 1. Ask and answer questions about key details in a text. **Literature 3.** Describe characters, settings, and major events in a story, using key details.

Next

2. Part A

What lesson does the author of the story want to teach?

○ **A.** Plants grow if you shout at them.

○ **B.** It is easy to make a garden.

○ **C.** You must wait for plants to grow.

○ **D.** Plants do not need much care.

Part B

Which detail from the story helps you know what lesson the story teaches?

○ **A.** "I wish I had a garden," said Toad.

○ **B.** "Soon your seeds will start to grow."

○ **C.** "It is very nice, but it was hard work."

○ **D.** "You are shouting too much," said Frog.

Copyright © Pearson Education, Inc., or its affiliates. All Rights Reserved.

COMMON CORE STATE STANDARDS

Literature 1. Ask and answer questions about key details in a text. **Literature 2.** Retell stories, including key details, and demonstrate understanding of their central message or lesson.

Next

Name _____

Vocabulary

Directions: Read the questions below and choose the best answer.

3. Part A

Which word in the story means the opposite of "softly"?

- ○ **A.** again
- ○ **B.** loudly
- ○ **C.** afraid
- ○ **D.** shouted

Part B

Which detail helps you choose the word in the story that means the opposite of "softly"?

- ○ **A.** "My seeds will not grow," said Toad.
- ○ **B.** **"Now seeds, start growing!"**
- ○ **C.** "My seeds are afraid to grow?" asked Toad.
- ○ **D.** Toad walked up and down a few times.

Copyright © Pearson Education, Inc., or its affiliates. All Rights Reserved.

COMMON CORE STATE STANDARDS

Literature 4. Identify words and phrases in stories or poems that suggest feelings or appeal to the senses.
Language 4.a. Use sentence-level context as a clue to the meaning of a word or phrase.

Next

4. Part A

In the following sentence, which words act together as a verb that tells about an action that will happen in the future?

"Soon your seeds will start to grow."

- ○ **A.** soon your
- ○ **B.** your seeds
- ○ **C.** seeds will
- ○ **D.** will start

Part B

Which word in this sentence helps you know that the action has not yet happened?

"Soon your seeds will start to grow."

- ○ **A.** seeds
- ○ **B.** soon
- ○ **C.** grow
- ○ **D.** your

Copyright © Pearson Education, Inc., or its affiliates. All Rights Reserved.

COMMON CORE STATE STANDARDS

Literature 4. Identify words and phrases in stories or poems that suggest feelings or appeal to the senses.
Language 1.e. Use verbs to convey a sense of past, present, and future (e.g., *Yesterday I walked home; Today I walk home; Tomorrow I will walk home*). **Language 4.a.** Use sentence-level context as a clue to the meaning of a word or phrase.

Next

Name _____

Writing — Constructed Response

Suppose Toad told you about his seeds. What would you tell him to do? Use details from the story to help you write.

_____

- -

_____

- -

_____

_____

- -

_____

_____

- -

_____

- -

_____

- -

_____

Copyright © Pearson Education, Inc., or its affiliates. All Rights Reserved.

To the Teacher: Use the Writing Rubric on page T19 to assess children's writing.

COMMON CORE STATE STANDARDS

Literature 1. Ask and answer questions about key details in a text. **Writing 2.** Write informative/ explanatory texts in which they name a topic, supply some facts about the topic, and provide some sense of closure. **Writing 8.** With guidance and support from adults, recall information from experiences or gather information from provided sources to answer a question.

Next

Writing — Extended Response

You have read two stories about growing plants.

- *Frog and Toad Together: The Garden*
- "Growing Plants"

What is easy about growing plants? What is not easy? Use details from *Frog and Toad Together: The Garden* and "Growing Plants" to help you answer the questions. Check your writing for correct capitalization, punctuation, and spelling.

Copyright © Pearson Education, Inc., or its affiliates. All Rights Reserved.

To the Teacher: Tell children they may use the space on this page to plan their writing. Then have them write their response on the following pages. Use the Writing Rubric on page T20 to assess children's writing.

COMMON CORE STATE STANDARDS

Informational Text 1. Ask and answer questions about key details in a text. **Writing 2.** Write informative/ explanatory texts in which they name a topic, supply some facts about the topic, and provide some sense of closure. **Writing 8.** With guidance and support from adults, recall information from experiences or gather information from provided sources to answer a question. **Language 1.** Demonstrate command of the conventions of standard English grammar and usage when writing or speaking. **Language 2.** Demonstrate command of the conventions of standard English capitalization, punctuation, and spelling when writing.

Next

Name _____

Copyright © Pearson Education, Inc., or its affiliates. All Rights Reserved.

Next

Copyright © Pearson Education, Inc., or its affiliates. All Rights Reserved.

Name _____

Directions: Read the following passage. Use information from the passage to answer the questions.

I'm a Caterpillar
by Jean Marzollo

I'm a caterpillar. Munch. Crunch.
I'm getting bigger! Munch. Crunch.
Munch. Crunch. Munch. Crunch.
That's it. No more food. I'm done.
It's time to hang from a stem.
I wait, and wait, and wait.
I shiver.
I twist.
I split my skin!
My old skin falls away.
I am soft inside.
I am a pupa.
I grow a shell to protect the pupa.
I am now a chrysalis.
I keep changing.
Soon I'll come out.
What will I be?
A butterfly!
Push. Crack. Wow! I'm free!

Copyright © Pearson Education, Inc., or its affiliates. All Rights Reserved.

Next

My wings are all wet.
My wings dry off. They unfold.
Flap. Flap. Hey! I can fly! Ta-da!
I visit flowers. I drink nectar. Yum!
My mouth is like a straw.
Sip. Sip. Sip.
I have a mate. We visit many flowers.
We're not afraid of birds.
They know that we taste awful.
Soon I will lay my eggs.
The eggs have thin shells.
Baby caterpillars crawl out.
Hi! I'm a caterpillar.
Munch. Crunch.

What will happen to me next?
Do you know?

Copyright © Pearson Education, Inc., or its affiliates. All Rights Reserved.

Name _____

Text-Based Comprehension

Directions: Read the questions below and choose the best answer.

1. Part A

What happens to the caterpillar next after it becomes a chrysalis?

○ **A.** It grows a shell.

○ **B.** It becomes a butterfly.

○ **C.** It visits flowers.

○ **D.** It drinks nectar.

Part B

Which word in the story helps you figure out what happens next after it becomes a chrysalis?

○ **A.** soon

○ **B.** I'll

○ **C.** what

○ **D.** out

Copyright © Pearson Education, Inc., or its affiliates. All Rights Reserved.

COMMON CORE STATE STANDARDS

Informational Text 1. Ask and answer questions about key details in a text. **Informational Text 3.** Describe the connection between two individuals, events, ideas, or pieces of information in a text.

Next

2. **Part A**

What will happen next to the caterpillar that talks at the end of the story?

○ **A.** It will become a pupa.

○ **B.** It will grow a shell.

○ **C.** It will turn to a butterfly.

○ **D.** It will lay eggs.

Part B

What fact helps you know what will happen to the caterpillar next?

○ **A.** Butterflies start out as caterpillars.

○ **B.** Baby caterpillars keep changing.

○ **C.** The caterpillar at the beginning becomes a pupa next.

○ **D.** No one knows what will happen to the caterpillar next.

Copyright © Pearson Education, Inc., or its affiliates. All Rights Reserved.

COMMON CORE STATE STANDARDS

Informational Text 1. Ask and answer questions about key details in a text. **Informational Text 3.** Describe the connection between two individuals, events, ideas, or pieces of information in a text.

Next

Name _____

Vocabulary

Directions: Read the questions below and choose the best answer.

3. Part A

What does "protect" mean in the following sentence?
"I grow a shell to protect the pupa."

○ **A.** keep safe

○ **B.** help something grow

○ **C.** make something bigger

○ **D.** wrap around

Part B

Which sentence from the passage helps you understand what "protect" means?

○ **A.** My old skin falls away.

○ **B.** I am soft inside.

○ **C.** I am a pupa.

○ **D.** I am now a chrysalis.

Copyright © Pearson Education, Inc., or its affiliates. All Rights Reserved.

COMMON CORE STATE STANDARDS

Informational Text 4. Ask and answer questions to help determine or clarify the meaning of words and phrases in a text. **Language 4.a.** Use sentence-level context as a clue to the meaning of a word or phrase.

Next

4. Part A

The caterpillar uses the words "munch" and "crunch." What is the caterpillar doing?

○ **A.** playing

○ **B.** flying

○ **C.** changing

○ **D.** eating

Part B

Which story sentence most helps you understand the meanings of "munch" and "crunch"?

○ **A.** I'm getting bigger!

○ **B.** No more food.

○ **C.** I'm done.

○ **D.** It's time to hang from a stem.

Copyright © Pearson Education, Inc., or its affiliates. All Rights Reserved.

COMMON CORE STATE STANDARDS

Informational Text 4. Ask and answer questions to help determine or clarify the meaning of words and phrases in a text. **Language 4.a.** Use sentence-level context as a clue to the meaning of a word or phrase.

Next

Name _____

Writing — Constructed Response

Pretend you are a butterfly. What is your favorite thing to do? Use facts and details from the story to help you write.

_____

_____

_____

_____

_____

_____

_____

_____

_____

_____

Copyright © Pearson Education, Inc., or its affiliates. All Rights Reserved.

To the Teacher: Use the Writing Rubric on page T19 to assess children's writing.

COMMON CORE STATE STANDARDS

Informational Text 1. Ask and answer questions about key details in a text. **Writing 2.** Write informative/explanatory texts in which they name a topic, supply some facts about the topic, and provide some sense of closure. **Writing 8.** With guidance and support from adults, recall information from experiences or gather information from provided sources to answer a question.

Next

Writing — Extended Response

You have read two stories about animals.

- *I'm a Caterpillar*
- *Life in the Forest*

How are caterpillars like ants and hummingbirds? How are they different? Use details from *I'm a Caterpillar* and *Life in the Forest* to help you answer the questions. Also use facts you already know. Check your writing for correct capitalization, punctuation, and spelling.

Copyright © Pearson Education, Inc., or its affiliates. All Rights Reserved.

To the Teacher: Tell children they may use the space on this page to plan their writing. Then have them write their response on the following pages. Use the Writing Rubric on page T20 to assess children's writing.

COMMON CORE STATE STANDARDS

Informational Text 1. Ask and answer questions about key details in a text. **Writing 2.** Write informative/ explanatory texts in which they name a topic, supply some facts about the topic, and provide some sense of closure. **Writing 8.** With guidance and support from adults, recall information from experiences or gather information from provided sources to answer a question. **Language 2.** Demonstrate command of the conventions of standard English capitalization, punctuation, and spelling when writing.

Next

Name _____

Copyright © Pearson Education, Inc., or its affiliates. All Rights Reserved.

Copyright © Pearson Education, Inc., or its affiliates. All Rights Reserved.

Name _____

Directions: Read the following passage. Use information from the passage to answer the questions.

Where Are My Animal Friends?

by William Chin

Characters	Raccoon Goose Bear Hummingbird Squirrel
Raccoon	Hello, Goose! Why are you shivering?
Goose	This forest is chilly, Raccoon. The days are shorter now. And it's getting colder every day.
Raccoon	Then we don't have much time to find our friends.
Goose	You're right, Raccoon. Let's look for Caterpillar.
Raccoon	Caterpillar lives in this tree. But where are all the leaves?
Goose	Many of them are on the ground. Where is Caterpillar? Look, here comes the smallest bird in the forest. Hello, Hummingbird! Have you seen Caterpillar?
Hummingbird	Oh, yes. Caterpillar is right here.

Copyright © Pearson Education, Inc., or its affiliates. All Rights Reserved.

Next

Raccoon	That's not Caterpillar! Caterpillar is long. This thing is not long.
Goose	Our friend Caterpillar moves a lot. This thing does not move at all.
Hummingbird	But Caterpillar is inside.
Goose	Then we won't see Caterpillar until spring, when he'll be a butterfly.
Raccoon	Well, I'm glad you will be here for the winter.
Goose	Oh, no, Raccoon. I can't stay. I must fly away to where it is warm. Hummingbird must too.
Hummingbird	Yes, we must go.
Raccoon	Oh, my! I am the saddest raccoon in the forest. Will you come back?
Goose	Yes, we'll be back in the spring. Good-bye, Raccoon!
Raccoon	Good-bye, Goose! Good-bye, Hummingbird!
	I will see if Bear is at home.
	Hello, Bear!

Copyright © Pearson Education, Inc., or its affiliates. All Rights Reserved.

Bear	Hello, Raccoon. Is it spring yet?
Raccoon	No, not yet. It will be winter before it is spring. Why are you sleeping?
Bear	I ate and ate all summer. Now I am fatter than before, and I don't need to eat. I will sleep a long time. I won't budge until spring.
Raccoon	Oh, no! All my friends are going away!
Bear	. . . Good night, Raccoon!
Raccoon	Good night, Bear. But who will be my friend? Oh, here comes Squirrel.
Squirrel	Hello, Raccoon. Where is everyone?
Raccoon	Goose flew away, and so did Hummingbird. We won't see Caterpillar until spring, and Bear is sleeping for the winter. Are you going away too?
Squirrel	Oh, no. I will stay here all winter. I have a warm nest and lots of food. Will you play with me?
Raccoon	Yes, Squirrel! Let's race to the edge of the forest and back!

Copyright © Pearson Education, Inc., or its affiliates. All Rights Reserved.

Next

Text-Based Comprehension

Directions: Read the questions below and choose the best answer.

I. Part A

How are Squirrel and Raccoon different from the other animals?

- ○ **A.** They are smaller than the others.
- ○ **B.** They go to warm places in winter.
- ○ **C.** They go away and sleep until spring.
- ○ **D.** They stay active in the forest all winter.

Part B

Which detail in the play most helps you know how Squirrel and Raccoon are different from other animals?

- ○ **A.** "Look, here comes the smallest bird in the forest."
- ○ **B.** "I am the saddest raccoon in the forest."
- ○ **C.** "Oh, no! All my friends are going away!"
- ○ **D.** "I must fly away to where it is warm."

Copyright © Pearson Education, Inc., or its affiliates. All Rights Reserved.

COMMON CORE STATE STANDARDS

Literature 1. Ask and answer questions about key details in a text. **Literature 3.** Describe characters, settings, and major events in a story, using key details.

Next

Name _____

2. Part A

What is the main idea of the play?

○ **A.** Forest animals don't have friends.

○ **B.** Some animals don't like cold weather.

○ **C.** Bears go to warm places in winter.

○ **D.** Caterpillars hide in winter.

Part B

Which detail from the play helps you know the main idea?

○ **A.** "We won't see Caterpillar until spring, and Bear is sleeping for the winter."

○ **B.** "Our friend Caterpillar moves a lot."

○ **C.** "I have a warm nest and lots of food."

○ **D.** "Let's race to the edge of the forest and back!"

Copyright © Pearson Education, Inc., or its affiliates. All Rights Reserved.

COMMON CORE STATE STANDARDS

Literature 1. Ask and answer questions about key details in a text. **Literature 3.** Describe characters, settings, and major events in a story, using key details.

Next

Vocabulary

Directions: Read the questions below and choose the best answer.

3. Part A

What does "shivering" mean in the following first line of the play?

"Why are you shivering?"

○ **A.** talking fast

○ **B.** climbing trees

○ **C.** jumping up and down

○ **D.** shaking from cold

Part B

Which word in the play is a clue to the meaning of "shivering"?

○ **A.** forest

○ **B.** chilly

○ **C.** days

○ **D.** shorter

Copyright © Pearson Education, Inc., or its affiliates. All Rights Reserved.

COMMON CORE STATE STANDARDS

Literature 4. Identify words and phrases in stories or poems that suggest feelings or appeal to the senses.
Language 4.a. Use sentence-level context as a clue to the meaning of a word or phrase.

Next

Name _____

4. Part A

Bear says, "I won't budge until spring." Which word in the play means about the same as "budge"?

○ **A.** move

○ **B.** stay

○ **C.** eat

○ **D.** flew

Part B

Which words from Bear's speech help you know which word in the play means about the same as "budge"?

○ **A.** ate and ate

○ **B.** sleep a long time

○ **C.** fatter than before

○ **D.** don't need to eat

Copyright © Pearson Education, Inc., or its affiliates. All Rights Reserved.

COMMON CORE STATE STANDARDS

Literature 4. Identify words and phrases in stories or poems that suggest feelings or appeal to the senses.
Language 4.a. Use sentence-level context as a clue to the meaning of a word or phrase.

Writing — Constructed Response

The animals will wake up or return in spring. What will the animals say to one another? Write a story. Tell what some animals do and say in spring. Use *Where Are My Animal Friends?* as a model.

_____

- -

_____

_____

- -

_____

_____

- -

_____

_____

- -

_____

_____

- -

_____

Copyright © Pearson Education, Inc., or its affiliates. All Rights Reserved.

To the Teacher: Use the Writing Rubric on page T19 to assess children's writing.

COMMON CORE STATE STANDARDS

Literature 1. Ask and answer questions about key details in a text. **Writing 3.** Write narratives in which they recount two or more appropriately sequenced events, include some details regarding what happened, use temporal words to signal event order, and provide some sense of closure.

Next

Name _____

Writing – Extended Response

You have read a play and a poem about animals in winter.

- *Where Are My Animal Friends?*
- "Where Do Fish Go in Winter?"

What do some animals do in winter? Why do they do it? Use details from *Where Are My Animal Friends?* and "Where Do Fish Go in Winter?" to answer the questions. Check your writing for correct capitalization, punctuation, and spelling.

Copyright © Pearson Education, Inc., or its affiliates. All Rights Reserved.

To the Teacher: Tell children they may use the space on this page to plan their writing. Then have them write their response on the following page. Use the Writing Rubric on page T20 to assess children's writing.

COMMON CORE STATE STANDARDS

Literature 1. Ask and answer questions about key details in a text. **Writing 2.** Write informative/ explanatory texts in which they name a topic, supply some facts about the topic, and provide some sense of closure. **Writing 8.** With guidance and support from adults, recall information from experiences or gather information from provided sources to answer a question. **Language 2.** Demonstrate command of the conventions of standard English capitalization, punctuation, and spelling when writing.

Next

Copyright © Pearson Education, Inc., or its affiliates. All Rights Reserved.

Name _____

Directions: Read the following passage. Use information from the passage to answer the questions.

Mama's Birthday Present

by Carmen Tafolla

Francisco ran into the garden. His grandmother was reading a book.

"Grandma! Grandma!" called Francisco. "Next Sunday is Mama's birthday! Mama always surprises me with a party for my birthday. Can we surprise Mama with a party?"

"That is a wonderful idea, Francisco," said Grandma. "Today is Monday. If we begin today, we will have seven days to plan a party."

"Mama always gives me a present for my birthday," said Francisco. "What present can I give Mama?"

"I don't know," said Grandma. "But don't worry. We can make a piñata to break. Your mama will enjoy that."

So Grandma and Francisco made a piñata.

On Tuesday, Francisco wondered about Mama's present. Francisco went to talk with Papa about Mama's birthday party.

"What present can I give Mama?" asked Francisco.

Copyright © Pearson Education, Inc., or its affiliates. All Rights Reserved.

Next

"I don't know," said Papa. "But don't worry. I can play my guitar. Your mama will enjoy that."

So Papa promised Francisco he would play his guitar.

On Wednesday, Francisco wondered about Mama's present. Francisco and his older brother went to invite Señora Molina to Mama's party. . . .

On Sunday, everyone came to the party. Mama was very surprised. Papa played his guitar. . . .

Everyone looked happy. Everyone except Francisco.

"Francisco, what is the matter?" asked Mama.

"I did not know what to give you for your birthday, Mama."

"Oh, Francisco," said Mama. "This party was the best present you could give me. No, the second best."

"Second best?" asked Francisco.

"Yes. The best present of all is having my family and friends here with me. That is the most wonderful part of a party!"

Mama gave Francisco a big hug. Then they all took turns hitting the piñata. The one who broke it was Francisco.

And Mama enjoyed that.

Copyright © Pearson Education, Inc., or its affiliates. All Rights Reserved.

Name _____

Text-Based Comprehension

Directions: Read the questions below and choose the best answer.

I. Part A

What does Francisco do right after he and Grandma make a piñata?

- ○ **A.** invites Señora Molina to the party
- ○ **B.** hugs Mama
- ○ **C.** breaks the piñata
- ○ **D.** talks to Papa about Mama's party

Part B

Which word or words from the story best help you know what Francisco does right after he and Grandma make a piñata?

- ○ **A.** So
- ○ **B.** But
- ○ **C.** On Tuesday
- ○ **D.** On Wednesday

Copyright © Pearson Education, Inc., or its affiliates. All Rights Reserved.

COMMON CORE STATE STANDARDS

Literature 1. Ask and answer questions about key details in a text. **Literature 3.** Describe characters, settings, and major events in a story, using key details.

Next

2. Part A

What does Francisco learn at the end of the story?

○ **A.** Parties are more fun with music.

○ **B.** He can break a piñata.

○ **C.** Not all presents are things.

○ **D.** Mama doesn't like presents.

Part B

Which detail in the story helps you know what Francisco learns at the end of the story?

○ **A.** Mama gave Francisco a big hug.

○ **B.** Then they all took turns hitting the piñata.

○ **C.** The one who broke it was Francisco.

○ **D.** "This party was the best present you could give me."

Copyright © Pearson Education, Inc., or its affiliates. All Rights Reserved.

COMMON CORE STATE STANDARDS

Literature 1. Ask and answer questions about key details in a text. **Literature 3.** Describe characters, settings, and major events in a story, using key details.

Vocabulary

Directions: Read the questions below and choose the best answer.

3. Part A

Which word means the same as "present" as it is used in the story?

○ **A.** surprise

○ **B.** today

○ **C.** gift

○ **D.** party

Part B

Which sentence from the story helps you know the meaning of the word "present"?

○ **A.** "Mama always gives me a present for my birthday," said Francisco.

○ **B.** "Mama always surprises me with a party for my birthday."

○ **C.** "If we begin today, we will have seven days to plan a party."

○ **D.** On Tuesday, Francisco wondered about Mama's present.

Copyright © Pearson Education, Inc., or its affiliates. All Rights Reserved.

COMMON CORE STATE STANDARDS

Language 4. Determine or clarify the meaning of unknown and multiple-meaning words and phrases based on *grade 1 reading and content,* choosing flexibly from an array of strategies. **Language 4.a.** Use sentence-level context as a clue to the meaning of a word or phrase.

Next

4. **Part A**

In which group does the word "guitar" belong?

○ **A.** words that name party games

○ **B.** words that name types of surprises

○ **C.** words that name musical instruments

○ **D.** words that name birthday presents

Part B

Which detail from the passage most helps you know which group the word "guitar" should be in?

○ **A.** Francisco went to talk with Papa about Mama's birthday party.

○ **B.** So Grandma and Francisco made a piñata.

○ **C.** So Papa promised Francisco he would play his guitar.

○ **D.** Francisco and his older brother went to invite Señora Molina to Mama's party.

Copyright © Pearson Education, Inc., or its affiliates. All Rights Reserved.

COMMON CORE STATE STANDARDS

Language 4. Determine or clarify the meaning of unknown and multiple-meaning words and phrases based on *grade 1 reading and content,* choosing flexibly from an array of strategies. **Language 5.a.** Sort words into categories (e.g., colors, clothing) to gain a sense of the concepts the categories represent.

Name _____

Writing — Constructed Response

Suppose you are planning a party for someone special. What surprise would you make? Tell how the surprise is like something in *Mama's Birthday Present*.

_____

_____

_____

_____

_____

_____

_____

_____

_____

_____

_____

_____

_____

Copyright © Pearson Education, Inc., or its affiliates. All Rights Reserved.

To the Teacher: Use the Writing Rubric on page T19 to assess children's writing.

COMMON CORE STATE STANDARDS

Literature 1. Ask and answer questions about key details in a text. **Writing 2.** Write informative/explanatory texts in which they name a topic, supply some facts about the topic, and provide some sense of closure. **Writing 8.** With guidance and support from adults, recall information from experiences or gather information from provided sources to answer a question.

Next

Writing — Extended Response

You have read two selections about parties.

- *Mama's Birthday Present*
- "Limonada Recipe"

What is your favorite part of a party? What special treat do you like to make or have at a party? Use details from *Mama's Birthday Present* and "Limonada Recipe" as examples in your writing. Check your writing for correct capitalization, punctuation, and spelling.

Copyright © Pearson Education, Inc., or its affiliates. All Rights Reserved.

To the Teacher: Tell children they may use the space on this page to plan their writing. Then have them write their response on the following pages. Use the Writing Rubric on page T20 to assess children's writing.

COMMON CORE STATE STANDARDS

Literature 1. Ask and answer questions about key details in a text. **Writing 1.** Write opinion pieces in which they introduce the topic or name the book they are writing about, state an opinion, supply a reason for the opinion, and provide some sense of closure. **Writing 8.** With guidance and support from adults, recall information from experiences or gather information from provided sources to answer a question. **Language 2.** Demonstrate command of the conventions of standard English capitalization, punctuation, and spelling when writing.

Next

Name _____

Copyright © Pearson Education, Inc., or its affiliates. All Rights Reserved.

Next

Copyright © Pearson Education, Inc., or its affiliates. All Rights Reserved.

Name _____

Directions: Read the following passage. Use information from the passage to answer the questions.

Cinderella
by Teresa R. Roberts

Once upon a time, in a far-off land, over hills and past farms, lived a girl named Cinderella. Cindy, as she was called, was sweet and nice.

Cindy had two sisters. Roz and Gert were not so sweet or nice. They were mean. They made Cindy sweep, mop, scrub, and dust all day.

Each year the prince had a great ball at his castle. One day, a man came with a note. The prince asked the sisters to his ball.

"Maybe he will make me his wife!" Gert clapped her hands. "No, he will not! It will be me!" Roz yelled.

"May I go as well?" asked Cindy. "No!" cried her sisters. . . .

Cindy watched Roz and Gert try on dresses. Red! Green! White! Pink! Such nice colors! And the finest fabric stitched with the finest thread! All Cindy got was a dirty mop.

Cindy watched her sisters drive off. She tried sweeping. She tried dusting. But she felt so sad. She hung her head and cried.

Copyright © Pearson Education, Inc., or its affiliates. All Rights Reserved.

Next

Rap, tap, tap. Rap, tap, tap. A wise old woman came in.

She patted Cindy's hand. "I will help you go to the ball."

"But I cannot go in these rags!" Cindy wailed.

"Just wait and see. I will show you."

Snap! Cindy had a nice dress and glass slippers! . . .

"It is time to go! But be back by twelve o'clock. The chimes will ring. That will be the sign that everything will turn back."

Cinderella went to the ball. She met the prince. They twirled and whirled in each other's arms all night.

Then the chimes started clanging. Cindy gasped and ran fast. "Wait!" called the prince. "Stop!"

He did not see where Cindy went. She had lost her glass slipper on the top step.

Back at home, Cindy's sisters made her scrub, sweep, and mop. She no longer wore her fine dress. . . .

Rap, tap, tap. It was the prince! "Is this your glass slipper?" he asked Roz. She tried it. It did not fit. Then Gert tried it. It did not fit.

But it *did* fit Cinderella. She and the prince married, and they lived happily ever after.

Copyright © Pearson Education, Inc., or its affiliates. All Rights Reserved.

Next

Name _____

Text-Based Comprehension

Directions: Read the questions below and choose the best answer.

1. Part A

Which part of the story best shows that it is a fairy tale and not a realistic story?

○ **A.** Roz and Gert are mean to Cindy.

○ **B.** Cindy cleans the house very well.

○ **C.** A prince invites people to a ball at his castle.

○ **D.** A wise old woman appears suddenly to help Cindy.

Part B

Which detail in the story helps you know that it is a fairy tale?

○ **A.** The prince asked the sisters to his ball.

○ **B.** *Snap!* Cindy had a nice dress and glass slippers!

○ **C.** Roz and Gert were not so sweet or nice.

○ **D.** They made Cindy sweep, mop, scrub, and dust all day.

Copyright © Pearson Education, Inc., or its affiliates. All Rights Reserved.

COMMON CORE STATE STANDARDS

Literature 1. Ask and answer questions about key details in a text. **Literature 3.** Describe characters, settings, and major events in a story, using key details.

Next

2. Part A

What is a theme of the fairy tale?

○ **A.** Good things happen to nice people.

○ **B.** People should not wear glass slippers.

○ **C.** It is fun to sweep and clean.

○ **D.** Everyone should live in a castle.

Part B

Which detail from the story helps you know what the theme is?

○ **A.** Each year the prince had a great ball at his castle.

○ **B.** They made Cindy sweep, mop, scrub, and dust all day.

○ **C.** She had lost her glass slipper on the top step.

○ **D.** She and the prince married, and they lived happily ever after.

Copyright © Pearson Education, Inc., or its affiliates. All Rights Reserved.

COMMON CORE STATE STANDARDS

Literature 1. Ask and answer questions about key details in a text. **Literature 3.** Describe characters, settings, and major events in a story, using key details.

Next

Name _____

Vocabulary

Directions: Read the questions below and choose the best answer.

3. **Part A**

Which word means about the same as "fabric" in the following sentences?

"Such nice colors! And the finest fabric stitched with the finest thread!"

- ○ **A.** style
- ○ **B.** cloth
- ○ **C.** buttons
- ○ **D.** jewels

Part B

Which word from the following sentences helps you know the meaning of the word "fabric"?

"Such nice colors! And the finest fabric stitched with the finest thread!"

- ○ **A.** nice
- ○ **B.** colors
- ○ **C.** finest
- ○ **D.** thread

Copyright © Pearson Education, Inc., or its affiliates. All Rights Reserved.

COMMON CORE STATE STANDARDS

Language 4. Determine or clarify the meaning of unknown and multiple-meaning words and phrases based on *grade 1 reading and content*, choosing flexibly from an array of strategies. **Language 4.a.** Use sentence-level context as a clue to the meaning of a word or phrase.

Next

4. Part A

What does "gasped" mean in the following sentence?
"Cindy gasped and ran fast."

- ○ **A.** laughed happily
- ○ **B.** spoke in a low voice
- ○ **C.** took a breath in alarm
- ○ **D.** danced slowly

Part B

Which detail from the story helps you know the meaning of the word "gasped"?

- ○ **A.** Cinderella went to the ball.
- ○ **B.** She met the prince.
- ○ **C.** They twirled and whirled in each other's arms all night.
- ○ **D.** Then the chimes started clanging.

Copyright © Pearson Education, Inc., or its affiliates. All Rights Reserved.

COMMON CORE STATE STANDARDS

Language 4. Determine or clarify the meaning of unknown and multiple-meaning words and phrases based on *grade 1 reading and content*, choosing flexibly from an array of strategies. **Language 4.a.** Use sentence-level context as a clue to the meaning of a word or phrase.

Next

Name _____

Writing – Constructed Response

People have been reading *Cinderella* for a very long time. Why do you think people like the story so much? Use examples from the story to support your ideas.

_____

- -

_____

- -

_____

- -

_____

- -

_____

- -

_____

- -

_____

- -

_____

- -

_____

Copyright © Pearson Education, Inc., or its affiliates. All Rights Reserved.

To the Teacher: Use the Writing Rubric on page T19 to assess children's writing.

COMMON CORE STATE STANDARDS

Literature 1. Ask and answer questions about key details in a text. **Writing 1.** Write opinion pieces in which they introduce the topic or name the book they are writing about, state an opinion, supply a reason for the opinion, and provide some sense of closure. **Writing 8.** With guidance and support from adults, recall information from experiences or gather information from provided sources to answer a question.

Next

Writing — Extended Response

You have read two fairy tales.

- "Anarosa"
- *Cinderella*

The two fairy tales are very much alike. Which one do you like better? Use details from "Anarosa" and *Cinderella* as examples in your writing. Check your writing for correct capitalization, punctuation, and spelling.

To the Teacher: Tell children they may use the space on this page to plan their writing. Then have them write their response on the following pages. Use the Writing Rubric on page T20 to assess children's writing.

COMMON CORE STATE STANDARDS

Literature 1. Ask and answer questions about key details in a text. **Writing 1.** Write opinion pieces in which they introduce the topic or name the book they are writing about, state an opinion, supply a reason for the opinion, and provide some sense of closure. **Writing 8.** With guidance and support from adults, recall information from experiences or gather information from provided sources to answer a question. **Language 2.** Demonstrate command of the conventions of standard English capitalization, punctuation, and spelling when writing.

Next

Copyright © Pearson Education, Inc., or its affiliates. All Rights Reserved.

Name _____

Copyright © Pearson Education, Inc., or its affiliates. All Rights Reserved.

Copyright © Pearson Education, Inc., or its affiliates. All Rights Reserved.

Name _____

Directions: Read the following passage. Use information from the passage to answer the questions.

A Trip to Washington, D.C.
by Elizabeth Fitzgerald Howard

Hi! My name is Metro Mike, and I'm here to show you Washington, D.C.! Every year people come to this city from all over. Do you know why? It is the capital of our country.

Come with me! I'll show you this splendid city. Sometimes I have a busload of people. But now this coach is just for you.

In Washington, D.C., the leaders of our country make laws. Laws are rules we follow. How do those people become our leaders? We vote for them. When people vote, they pick who will make the laws that we all follow.

Our first stop is on your left. That's the home of two documents. One is the Declaration of Independence. That paper says that Americans have the right to be free. The other is the U.S. Constitution. It is the plan for our government.

Washington, D.C., was named after George Washington, our first President. The President is the leader of our country. Many people call George Washington the "Father of Our Country."

Copyright © Pearson Education, Inc., or its affiliates. All Rights Reserved.

Next

I'll slow down here to show you the White House. This is where the President lives and works now.

This next road will take us by the Potomac River. Look up in the sky! That beautiful bird stands for America. It is strong and free!

Did you see that splash? That bird took a fish to put in its mouth. Once there weren't many of these birds in the wild. Now there are many more.

Down that street you'll see lots of flags! In Washington, D.C., you will see the Stars and Stripes flying in many places. This red, white, and blue flag also stands for America.

We are back at the start. I hope you found Washington, D.C., to be a great city. Come back again soon!

Copyright © Pearson Education, Inc., or its affiliates. All Rights Reserved.

Next

Text-Based Comprehension

Directions: Read the questions below and choose the best answer.

1. **Part A**

   What is the main topic of the passage?

   ○ **A.** the first President of the United States

   ○ **B.** the beauty of nature in Washington

   ○ **C.** things to see in our nation's capital

   ○ **D.** how laws are made in our country

   Part B

   Which sentence helps you figure out the main topic of the passage?

   ○ **A.** This next road will take us by the Potomac River.

   ○ **B.** In Washington, D.C., the leaders of our country make laws.

   ○ **C.** Washington, D.C., was named after George Washington, our first President.

   ○ **D.** My name is Metro Mike, and I'm here to show you Washington, D.C.!

Copyright © Pearson Education, Inc., or its affiliates. All Rights Reserved.

COMMON CORE STATE STANDARDS

Informational Text 1. Ask and answer questions about key details in a text. **Informational Text 2.** Identify the main topic and retell key details of a text.

Next

2. Part A

What is one reason visitors go to see the documents in Washington, D.C.?

○ **A.** The documents remind people of their rights.

○ **B.** The documents are worth much money.

○ **C.** The documents were written by George Washington.

○ **D.** The documents tell people how to vote.

Part B

Which sentence from the passage helps you know one reason visitors go to see the documents?

○ **A.** I'll show you this splendid city.

○ **B.** Many people call George Washington the "Father of Our Country."

○ **C.** When people vote, they pick who will make the laws that we all follow.

○ **D.** That paper says that Americans have the right to be free.

Copyright © Pearson Education, Inc., or its affiliates. All Rights Reserved.

COMMON CORE STATE STANDARDS

Informational Text 1. Ask and answer questions about key details in a text. **Informational Text 3.** Describe the connection between two individuals, events, ideas, or pieces of information in a text.

Next

Name _____

Vocabulary

Directions: Read the questions below and choose the best answer.

3. **Part A**

What does "capital" mean in the following sentence?
"It is the capital of our country."

○ **A.** the most important city

○ **B.** the city where laws are made

○ **C.** the place with the most flags

○ **D.** the city with the most visitors

Part B

Which sentence from the passage helps you understand what the word "capital" means?

○ **A.** Every year people come to this city from all over.

○ **B.** I'll show you this splendid city.

○ **C.** In Washington, D.C., the leaders of our country make laws.

○ **D.** In Washington, D.C., you will see the Stars and Stripes flying in many places.

Copyright © Pearson Education, Inc., or its affiliates. All Rights Reserved.

COMMON CORE STATE STANDARDS

Informational Text 4. Ask and answer questions to help determine or clarify the meaning of words and phrases in a text. **Language 4.** Determine or clarify the meaning of unknown and multiple-meaning words and phrases based on *grade 1 reading and content,* choosing flexibly from an array of strategies. **Language 4.a.** Use sentence-level context as a clue to the meaning of a word or phrase.

Next

4. Part A

What does the word "documents" mean in the following sentence?

"That's the home of two documents."

○ **A.** important pages

○ **B.** things from history

○ **C.** buildings

○ **D.** maps of a city

Part B

What is one sentence from the passage that helps you know the meaning of the word "documents"?

○ **A.** Laws are rules we follow.

○ **B.** That paper says that Americans have the right to be free.

○ **C.** I'll slow down here to show you the White House.

○ **D.** This next road will take us by the Potomac River.

Copyright © Pearson Education, Inc., or its affiliates. All Rights Reserved.

COMMON CORE STATE STANDARDS

Language 4. Determine or clarify the meaning of unknown and multiple-meaning words and phrases based on *grade 1 reading and content,* choosing flexibly from an array of strategies. **Language 4.a.** Use sentence-level context as a clue to the meaning of a word or phrase.

Next

Name _____

Writing — Constructed Response

Suppose you took a trip to Washington, D.C. What would you most like to see and do? Use details from the story to help you write.

_____
- -
_____
- -
_____
- -
_____
- -
_____
- -
_____
- -
_____
- -
_____
- -
_____
- -
_____
- -
_____

Copyright © Pearson Education, Inc., or its affiliates. All Rights Reserved.

To the Teacher: Use the Writing Rubric on page T19 to assess children's writing.

COMMON CORE STATE STANDARDS

Informational Text 1. Ask and answer questions about key details in a text. **Writing 2.** Write informative/ explanatory texts in which they name a topic, supply some facts about the topic, and provide some sense of closure. **Writing 8.** With guidance and support from adults, recall information from experiences or gather information from provided sources to answer a question.

Next

Writing — Extended Response

You have read two selections about our country and showing our feelings about it.

- "My 4th of July"
- *A Trip to Washington, D.C.*

What are two ways you show your feelings for your country? Use details from the selections to help you answer the questions. Also use facts you already know. Check your writing for correct capitalization, punctuation, and spelling.

To the Teacher: Tell children they may use the space on this page to plan their writing. Then have them write their response on the following pages. Use the Writing Rubric on page T20 to assess children's writing.

COMMON CORE STATE STANDARDS

Informational Text 1. Ask and answer questions about key details in a text. **Writing 2.** Write informative/ explanatory texts in which they name a topic, supply some facts about the topic, and provide some sense of closure. **Writing 8.** With guidance and support from adults, recall information from experiences or gather information from provided sources to answer a question. **Language 2.** Demonstrate command of the conventions of standard English capitalization, punctuation, and spelling when writing.

Copyright © Pearson Education, Inc., or its affiliates. All Rights Reserved.

Next

Name _____

Copyright © Pearson Education, Inc., or its affiliates. All Rights Reserved.

Next

Copyright © Pearson Education, Inc., or its affiliates. All Rights Reserved.

Name _____

Directions: Read the following passage. Use information from the passage to answer the questions.

A Southern Ranch
by Yossel Ayarzagoitia Riesenfeld

The sun isn't up yet, and high above the land, the moon still gleams in dark skies. But lights are on in this place. Another day is starting on the ranch.

Ranches are places that raise livestock. Horses, cows, sheep, and goats are livestock. This ranch raises cows, or cattle. Ranch hands help look after the livestock and the ranch.

Ranch hands no longer take cattle up long trails. Ranch hands may drive pickup trucks. But they are still much like ranch hands long ago.

Ranch hands still ride horses and use lassos. They still care for sick animals. Ranch hands still watch herds of cattle.

If cattle go the wrong way, ranch hands must lead them the right way. In summer, if herds eat all the grass in one place, ranch hands take them to another place. In winter, ranch hands feed herds hay and grain.

Copyright © Pearson Education, Inc., or its affiliates. All Rights Reserved.

Next

Roundups take place in spring and fall. Ranch hands go out in the field and look for cows. This is not an easy job. Cows might be standing under a tree or grazing at the bottom of a hill.

After getting eight or ten cows, ranch hands must keep them together and keep them walking. Cows might run off. Ranch hands must chase them and bring them back.

Ranch hands need well-trained horses for this work. These horses can be steered by just a touch, and they know cows!

Sometimes cattle dogs help keep the cows together too.

Ranch hands bring small bunches of cows to the same spot. Nine or ten become forty or fifty.

Then ranch hands bring those bigger bunches to another spot. In time, the herd might number 600 or more.

Keeping this big herd together is hard.

Copyright © Pearson Education, Inc., or its affiliates. All Rights Reserved.

Next

Name _____

Text-Based Comprehension

Directions: Read the questions below and choose the best answer.

1. Part A

What do ranch hands do in summer?

○ **A.** They put cattle into groups.

○ **B.** They feed cattle hay.

○ **C.** They help cattle get food.

○ **D.** They take the cattle to sell.

Part B

Which sentence from the passage most helps you know what ranch hands do in the summer?

○ **A.** Roundups take place in spring and fall.

○ **B.** Ranch hands go out in the field and look for cows.

○ **C.** In summer, if herds eat all the grass in one place, ranch hands take them to another place.

○ **D.** In winter, ranch hands feed herds hay and grain.

Copyright © Pearson Education, Inc., or its affiliates. All Rights Reserved.

COMMON CORE STATE STANDARDS

Informational Text 1. Ask and answer questions about key details in a text. **Informational Text 3.** Describe the connection between two individuals, events, ideas, or pieces of information in a text.

Next

2. Part A

Which is a main idea of the passage?

- ○ **A.** There are few ranches today.
- ○ **B.** It is fun to visit a ranch.
- ○ **C.** A ranch hand's work is hard.
- ○ **D.** Ranch hands help plant crops.

Part B

Which detail from the passage supports the main idea?

- ○ **A.** Ranch hands must chase them [cows] and bring them back.
- ○ **B.** Ranch hands no longer take cattle up long trails.
- ○ **C.** Ranch hands may drive pickup trucks.
- ○ **D.** Ranch hands need well-trained horses for this work.

Copyright © Pearson Education, Inc., or its affiliates. All Rights Reserved.

COMMON CORE STATE STANDARDS

Informational Text 1. Ask and answer questions about key details in a text. **Informational Text 2.** Identify the main topic and retell key details of a text.

Next

Name _____

Vocabulary

Directions: Read the questions below and choose the best answer.

3. **Part A**

   What does "hands" mean in the passage? Look at the following example.

   "Ranch hands go out in the field and look for cows."

   ○ **A.** body parts

   ○ **B.** trucks

   ○ **C.** crops

   ○ **D.** workers

   Part B

   Which sentence from the passage does **not** help you understand what "hands" means?

   ○ **A.** Another day is starting on the ranch.

   ○ **B.** Ranch hands help look after the livestock and the ranch.

   ○ **C.** In winter, ranch hands feed herds hay and grain.

   ○ **D.** Ranch hands go out in the field and look for cows.

Copyright © Pearson Education, Inc., or its affiliates. All Rights Reserved.

COMMON CORE STATE STANDARDS

Language 4. Determine or clarify the meaning of unknown and multiple-meaning words and phrases based on *grade 1 reading and content,* choosing flexibly from an array of strategies. **Language 4.a.** Use sentence-level context as a clue to the meaning of a word or phrase.

Next

4. Part A

What does "herds" mean in the passage in the following sentence?

"Ranch hands still watch herds of cattle."

- ○ **A.** pairs
- ○ **B.** helpers
- ○ **C.** groups
- ○ **D.** animals

Part B

Which word from the passage helps you understand what "herds" means?

- ○ **A.** cows
- ○ **B.** bunches
- ○ **C.** hands
- ○ **D.** roundups

Copyright © Pearson Education, Inc., or its affiliates. All Rights Reserved.

COMMON CORE STATE STANDARDS

Language 4. Determine or clarify the meaning of unknown and multiple-meaning words and phrases based on *grade 1 reading and content,* choosing flexibly from an array of strategies. **Language 4.a.** Use sentence-level context as a clue to the meaning of a word or phrase.

Next

Name _____

Writing — Constructed Response

Which part of being a ranch hand would you like? Which part would you not like? Use details from the story to help you write.

_____

- -

_____

- -

_____

- -

_____

- -

_____

- -

_____

- -

_____

- -

_____

Copyright © Pearson Education, Inc., or its affiliates. All Rights Reserved.

To the Teacher: Use the Writing Rubric on page T19 to assess children's writing.

COMMON CORE STATE STANDARDS

Informational Text 1. Ask and answer questions about key details in a text. **Writing 1.** Write opinion pieces in which they introduce the topic or name the book they are writing about, state an opinion, supply a reason for the opinion, and provide some sense of closure. **Writing 8.** With guidance and support from adults, recall information from experiences or gather information from provided sources to answer a question.

Next

Writing — Extended Response

You have read two selections about ranches.

- *A Southern Ranch*
- "On the Way to a Ranch"

Imagine you are visiting a ranch. What is the trip like? What do you see when you get there? Use details from the selections to help you answer the questions. Check your writing for correct capitalization, punctuation, and spelling.

Copyright © Pearson Education, Inc., or its affiliates. All Rights Reserved.

To the Teacher: Tell children they may use the space on this page to plan their writing. Then have them write their response on the following pages. Use the Writing Rubric on page T20 to assess children's writing.

COMMON CORE STATE STANDARDS

Informational Text 1. Ask and answer questions about key details in a text. **Writing 2.** Write informative/ explanatory texts in which they name a topic, supply some facts about the topic, and provide some sense of closure. **Writing 8.** With guidance and support from adults, recall information from experiences or gather information from provided sources to answer a question. **Language 2.** Demonstrate command of the conventions of standard English capitalization, punctuation, and spelling when writing.

Next

Name _____

Copyright © Pearson Education, Inc., or its affiliates. All Rights Reserved.

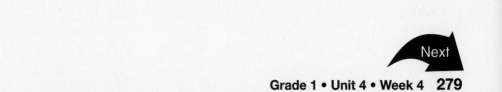

Copyright © Pearson Education, Inc., or its affiliates. All Rights Reserved.

Name _____

Directions: Read the following passage. Use information from the passage to answer the questions.

Peter's Chair
by Ezra Jack Keats

Peter stretched as high as he could. There! His tall building was finished.

CRASH! Down it came.

"Shhhh!" called his mother. "You'll have to play more quietly. Remember, we have a new baby in the house."

Peter looked into his sister Susie's room. His mother was fussing around the cradle. "That's my cradle," he thought, "and they painted it pink!"

"Hi, Peter," said his father. "Would you like to help paint Sister's high chair?" "It's my high chair," whispered Peter.

He saw his crib and muttered, "My crib. It's painted pink too."

Not far away stood his old chair.

"They didn't paint that yet!" Peter shouted.

He picked it up and ran to his room.

"Let's run away, Willie," he said. Peter filled a shopping bag with cookies and dog biscuits.

Copyright © Pearson Education, Inc., or its affiliates. All Rights Reserved.

Next

"We'll take my blue chair, my toy crocodile, and the picture of me when I was a baby."

Willie got his bone.

They went outside and stood in front of his house. "This is a good place," said Peter. He arranged his things very nicely and decided to sit in his chair for a while.

But he couldn't fit in the chair. He was too big!

His mother came to the window and called, "Won't you come back to us, Peter dear? We have something very special for lunch."

Peter and Willie made believe they didn't hear. But Peter got an idea.

Soon his mother saw signs that Peter was home. "That rascal is hiding behind the curtain," she said happily.

She moved the curtain away. But he wasn't there!

"Here I am," shouted Peter.

Peter sat in a grown-up chair. His father sat next to him.

"Daddy," said Peter, "let's paint the little chair pink for Susie."

And they did.

Copyright © Pearson Education, Inc., or its affiliates. All Rights Reserved.

Next

Name _____

Text-Based Comprehension

Directions: Read the questions below and choose the best answer.

1. Part A

How does Peter feel about his new sister at the beginning of the story?

◯ **A.** He is excited because he wants to help her.

◯ **B.** He is sad because he can't play with her yet.

◯ **C.** He is mad because she is taking his place.

◯ **D.** He is happy because she is cute.

Part B

Which sentence from the story best helps you know how Peter feels about his new sister at the beginning of the story?

◯ **A.** "Remember, we have a new baby in the house."

◯ **B.** "That's my cradle," he thought, "and they painted it pink!"

◯ **C.** Peter looked into his sister Susie's room.

◯ **D.** Peter stretched as high as he could.

Copyright © Pearson Education, Inc., or its affiliates. All Rights Reserved.

COMMON CORE STATE STANDARDS

Literature 1. Ask and answer questions about key details in a text. **Literature 3.** Describe characters, settings, and major events in a story, using key details.

Next

2. **Part A**

What is the main theme of the story?

○ **A.** Babies are fun.

○ **B.** Babies need many things.

○ **C.** Everyone grows up.

○ **D.** People shouldn't hide.

Part B

Which sentence from the story helps you know what the main theme of the story is?

○ **A.** Peter sat in a grown-up chair.

○ **B.** Peter and Willie made believe they didn't hear.

○ **C.** "Would you like to help paint Sister's high chair?"

○ **D.** "That rascal is hiding behind the curtain," she said happily.

Copyright © Pearson Education, Inc., or its affiliates. All Rights Reserved.

COMMON CORE STATE STANDARDS

Literature 1. Ask and answer questions about key details in a text. **Literature 2.** Retell stories, including key details, and demonstrate understanding of their central message or lesson.

Next

Name _____

Vocabulary

Directions: Read the questions below and choose the best answer.

3. Part A

What does Peter's mother mean when she uses the word "rascal" in the following sentence?

"That rascal is hiding behind the curtain," she said happily.

- ○ **A.** She thinks Peter is proud.
- ○ **B.** She thinks Peter is sad.
- ○ **C.** She thinks Peter is mean.
- ○ **D.** She thinks Peter is playful.

Part B

Which word in the following sentence helps you figure out what Peter's mother feels when she uses the word "rascal"?

"That rascal is hiding behind the curtain," she said happily.

- ○ **A.** behind
- ○ **B.** hiding
- ○ **C.** curtain
- ○ **D.** happily

Copyright © Pearson Education, Inc., or its affiliates. All Rights Reserved.

COMMON CORE STATE STANDARDS

Language 4. Determine or clarify the meaning of unknown and multiple-meaning words and phrases based on *grade 1 reading and content,* choosing flexibly from an array of strategies. **Language 4.a.** Use sentence-level context as a clue to the meaning of a word or phrase.

Next

4. Part A

What does the author show by the word "muttered" in the following sentences from the story?

He saw his crib and muttered, "My crib. It's painted pink too."

○ **A.** Peter is grumpy.

○ **B.** Peter is happy.

○ **C.** Peter is sleepy.

○ **D.** Peter is friendly.

Part B

Which other sentence from the story helps you know why the author used the word "muttered"?

○ **A.** Peter looked into his sister Susie's room.

○ **B.** His tall building was finished.

○ **C.** "Would you like to help paint Sister's high chair?"

○ **D.** "That's my cradle," he thought, "and they painted it pink!"

Copyright © Pearson Education, Inc., or its affiliates. All Rights Reserved.

COMMON CORE STATE STANDARDS

Language 4. Determine or clarify the meaning of unknown and multiple-meaning words and phrases based on *grade 1 reading and content,* choosing flexibly from an array of strategies. **Language 4.a.** Use sentence-level context as a clue to the meaning of a word or phrase.

Next

Name _____

Writing — Constructed Response

What is a grown-up thing you have done? How was it like what Peter did? Tell about what you did. Use examples from *Peter's Chair* in your writing.

_____

- -

_____

- -

_____

- -

_____

- -

_____

_____

- -

_____

_____

- -

_____

_____

- -

_____

Copyright © Pearson Education, Inc., or its affiliates. All Rights Reserved.

To the Teacher: Use the Writing Rubric on page T19 to assess children's writing.

COMMON CORE STATE STANDARDS

Literature 1. Ask and answer questions about key details in a text. **Writing 2.** Write informative/explanatory texts in which they name a topic, supply some facts about the topic, and provide some sense of closure. **Writing 8.** With guidance and support from adults, recall information from experiences or gather information from provided sources to answer a question.

Next

Writing — Extended Response

You have read two selections about getting a new sister.

- *Peter's Chair*
- "Peter's Baby Sister"

Suppose you got a new sister or brother. Write a letter to a friend or family member. Tell the person about the new baby. Use details from *Peter's Chair.* Use "Peter's Baby Sister" as a model for your letter. Check your writing for correct capitalization, punctuation, and spelling.

Copyright © Pearson Education, Inc., or its affiliates. All Rights Reserved.

To the Teacher: Tell children they may use the space on this page to plan their writing. Then have them write their response on the following pages. Use the Writing Rubric on page T20 to assess children's writing.

COMMON CORE STATE STANDARDS

Literature 1. Ask and answer questions about key details in a text. **Writing 2.** Write informative/explanatory texts in which they name a topic, supply some facts about the topic, and provide some sense of closure. **Writing 8.** With guidance and support from adults, recall information from experiences or gather information from provided sources to answer a question. **Language 2.** Demonstrate command of the conventions of standard English capitalization, punctuation, and spelling when writing.

Next

Name _____

Copyright © Pearson Education, Inc., or its affiliates. All Rights Reserved.

Copyright © Pearson Education, Inc., or its affiliates. All Rights Reserved.

Directions: Read the following passage. Use information from the passage to answer the questions.

Henry and Mudge and Mrs. Hopper's House (Part I)

by Cynthia Rylant

A Sweetheart Dance

Valentine's Day was coming. Henry and his big dog Mudge loved Valentine's Day because of the candy. They liked the candy hearts that said "You're swell" and "Oh, dear" and things like that.

Henry read the words, and Mudge licked them off. They were a good team.

On this Valentine's Day Henry's father and Henry's mother were going to a Sweetheart Dance. Henry and Mudge would be staying with Mrs. Hopper.

Mrs. Hopper lived across the street in a big stone house with droopy trees and dark windows and a gargoyle on the door.

Henry liked Mrs. Hopper. But he did not like her house.

"Are you sure Mudge and I can't come to the Sweetheart Dance?" Henry asked his father.

Copyright © Pearson Education, Inc., or its affiliates. All Rights Reserved.

Next

"Only if you both promise to wear a tuxedo and shiny black shoes and waltz to 'The Blue Danube,'" said Henry's father.

Henry looked at Mudge and tried to imagine him in a tuxedo and shiny black shoes, waltzing to "The Blue Danube."

"I think we'd better go to Mrs. Hopper's," Henry said.

"Good idea," said Henry's father.

"Because Mudge only knows how to tap-dance," Henry said with a grin.

Copyright © Pearson Education, Inc., or its affiliates. All Rights Reserved.

Name _____

Text-Based Comprehension

Directions: Read the questions below and choose the best answer.

I. Part A

What is Henry's main problem in the story?

- ○ **A.** He wants to be with Mudge on Valentine's Day.
- ○ **B.** He doesn't like Valentine's Day.
- ○ **C.** He doesn't want to stay with Mrs. Hopper.
- ○ **D.** He wants to go to the Sweetheart Dance.

Part B

Which sentence from the story helps you know what caused the problem?

- ○ **A.** Henry and Mudge would be staying with Mrs. Hopper.
- ○ **B.** But he did not like her house.
- ○ **C.** Henry read the words, and Mudge licked them off.
- ○ **D.** On this Valentine's Day Henry's father and Henry's mother were going to a Sweetheart Dance.

Copyright © Pearson Education, Inc., or its affiliates. All Rights Reserved.

COMMON CORE STATE STANDARDS

Literature 1. Ask and answer questions about key details in a text. **Literature 3.** Describe characters, settings, and major events in a story, using key details.

Next

2. Part A

How are Henry and his father alike?

○ **A.** They both like to make jokes.

○ **B.** They both like candy hearts.

○ **C.** They both dislike Mrs. Hopper's house.

○ **D.** They both dislike waltzing.

Part B

Which detail from the story helps you know how Henry is like his father?

○ **A.** "Are you sure Mudge and I can't come to the Sweetheart Dance?" Henry asked his father.

○ **B.** "Because Mudge only knows how to tap-dance," Henry said with a grin.

○ **C.** "I think we'd better go to Mrs. Hopper's," Henry said.

○ **D.** Henry and his big dog Mudge loved Valentine's Day because of the candy.

Copyright © Pearson Education, Inc., or its affiliates. All Rights Reserved.

COMMON CORE STATE STANDARDS

Literature 1. Ask and answer questions about key details in a text. **Literature 3.** Describe characters, settings, and major events in a story, using key details.

Next

Vocabulary

Directions: Read the questions below and choose the best answer.

3. **Part A**

What is the most likely meaning of "gargoyle" in the following sentence?

"Mrs. Hopper lived across the street in a big stone house with droopy trees and dark windows and a gargoyle on the door."

- ○ **A.** a scary decoration
- ○ **B.** a doorbell
- ○ **C.** a small window
- ○ **D.** a Valentine's Day heart

Part B

Which detail from the story helps you know the meaning of the word "gargoyle"?

- ○ **A.** Valentine's Day
- ○ **B.** Sweetheart Dance
- ○ **C.** big stone house
- ○ **D.** dark windows

Copyright © Pearson Education, Inc., or its affiliates. All Rights Reserved.

COMMON CORE STATE STANDARDS

Language 4. Determine or clarify the meaning of unknown and multiple-meaning words and phrases based on *grade 1 reading and content,* choosing flexibly from an array of strategies. **Language 4.a.** Use sentence-level context as a clue to the meaning of a word or phrase.

Next

4. Part A

What is a "tuxedo," as it is used in the following sentence?

"Only if you both promise to wear a tuxedo and shiny black shoes and waltz to 'The Blue Danube,'" said Henry's father.

○ **A.** an outfit for swimming

○ **B.** a type of dance

○ **C.** a fancy suit

○ **D.** a dog costume

Part B

Which detail from the passage helps you choose the answer for the meaning of the word "tuxedo"?

○ **A.** The Blue Danube

○ **B.** tap-dance

○ **C.** tried to imagine

○ **D.** shiny black shoes

Copyright © Pearson Education, Inc., or its affiliates. All Rights Reserved.

COMMON CORE STATE STANDARDS

Language 4. Determine or clarify the meaning of unknown and multiple-meaning words and phrases based on *grade 1 reading and content,* choosing flexibly from an array of strategies. **Language 4.a.** Use sentence-level context as a clue to the meaning of a word or phrase.

Next

Name _____

Writing — Constructed Response

Henry and Mudge like Valentine's Day. Do you like Valentine's Day? Write about why you do or do not like Valentine's Day. Use details from the story and your own ideas in your writing.

_____

_____

_____

_____

_____

_____

_____

_____

_____

Copyright © Pearson Education, Inc., or its affiliates. All Rights Reserved.

To the Teacher: Use the Writing Rubric on page T19 to assess children's writing.

COMMON CORE STATE STANDARDS

Literature 1. Ask and answer questions about key details in a text. **Writing 1.** Write opinion pieces in which they introduce the topic or name the book they are writing about, state an opinion, supply a reason for the opinion, and provide some sense of closure. **Writing 8.** With guidance and support from adults, recall information from experiences or gather information from provided sources to answer a question.

Next

Writing — Extended Response

You have read a story and a poem about reading stories.

- *Henry and Mudge and Mrs. Hopper's House*
- "Reading"

The poem "Reading" says, "A story is a special thing." The poet says the stories she has read stay inside her head. What is special about the story *Henry and Mudge and Mrs. Hopper's House?* What parts of the story will stay inside your head? Use details from *Henry and Mudge and Mrs. Hopper's House* and "Reading" as examples in your writing. Check your writing for correct capitalization, punctuation, and spelling.

To the Teacher: Tell children they may use the space on this page to plan their writing. Then have them write their response on the following pages. Use the Writing Rubric on page T20 to assess children's writing.

Copyright © Pearson Education, Inc., or its affiliates. All Rights Reserved.

COMMON CORE STATE STANDARDS

Literature 1. Ask and answer questions about key details in a text. **Writing 2.** Write informative/explanatory texts in which they name a topic, supply some facts about the topic, and provide some sense of closure. **Writing 8.** With guidance and support from adults, recall information from experiences or gather information from provided sources to answer a question. **Language 2.** Demonstrate command of the conventions of standard English capitalization, punctuation, and spelling when writing.

Next

Name _____

Copyright © Pearson Education, Inc., or its affiliates. All Rights Reserved.

Next

Copyright © Pearson Education, Inc., or its affiliates. All Rights Reserved.

Name _____

Directions: Read the following passage. Use information from the passage to answer the questions.

Tippy-Toe Chick, GO!
by George Shannon

Every morning when the dew had dried, Hen took her chicks to the garden for their favorite treat—sweet itty-bitty beans and potato bugs. Hen, Big Chick, and Middle Chick next, with Little Chick trailing along behind. Stopping to wonder at this and that. . . . Till ONE day—

RUFF-RUFF-RUFF-RUFF-RUFF! A big, grumpy dog came running their way, barking and growling at the end of a rope. Hen jumped back and pulled her chicks near. "There's no safe way to the beans today. We'll just have to wait for chicken feed." All three chicks said, "Bleck!" and frowned. "We're hungry!" . . .

Big Chick said, "Wait. I'LL take care of this." He slowly took a step toward Dog. "Now listen," he called. "We won't hurt you. We're just going to the garden for an itty-bitty treat."

RUFF-RUFF-RUFF-RUFF-RUFF! Dog disagreed, barking and pulling at the end of his rope. Big Chick ran to hide under Hen's safe wing.

Middle Chick took a breath, then stepped toward Dog. "I'M hungry, so YOU'D better stop it right now! Or YOU'LL be sorry when we get hold of you."

Copyright © Pearson Education, Inc., or its affiliates. All Rights Reserved.

Next

RUFF-RUFF-RUFF-RUFF-RUFF! Dog disagreed, barking and pulling at the end of his rope. Middle Chick ran to hide under Hen's safe wing.

"Let's go," said Hen. "We'll really have to wait." Little Chick peeped, "*I* want to try." "Oh, no!" said Hen, as the other chicks laughed. "You're much too small." Little Chick yelled, "But *I* can RUN!" . . .

Hen screamed and grabbed her heart. Big Chick closed his eyes. Middle Chick shook. Little Chick ran, *tippy-toe, tippy-toe,* without stopping to rest till she felt Dog's breath.

Then Little Chick laughed and began to run again. *Tippy-toe, tippy-toe* around the tree. Dog chased after her, tugging at his rope. RUFF-RUFF-RUFF-RUFF-RUFF! *Tippy-toe, tippy-toe* around the tree. . . . Till . . .

RUFF-RUP-yip-yip-yip-yip! Dog's rope was wrapped all around the tree. He was stuck and too mad to think "back up." Hen clucked with pride. Big Chick and Middle Chick just stood and stared.

Little Chick called, "It's time to eat!"

And off they ran, *tippy-toe, tippy-toe.* Right past Dog and into the garden for their favorite treat — sweet itty-bitty beans and potato bugs.

"YUM!"

Copyright © Pearson Education, Inc., or its affiliates. All Rights Reserved.

Next

Name _____

Text-Based Comprehension

Directions: Read the questions below and choose the best answer.

1. Part A

What main problem do Hen and her chicks have?

○ **A.** The chicks are making trouble.

○ **B.** Dog won't let them get food.

○ **C.** People won't bring chicken feed.

○ **D.** There is no food in the garden.

Part B

Which sentence from the story best helps you know what problem Hen and her chicks have?

○ **A.** "We're just going to the garden for an itty-bitty treat."

○ **B.** "We'll just have to wait for chicken feed."

○ **C.** A big, grumpy dog came running their way, barking and growling at the end of a rope.

○ **D.** All three chicks said, "Bleck!" and frowned.

Copyright © Pearson Education, Inc., or its affiliates. All Rights Reserved.

COMMON CORE STATE STANDARDS

Literature 1. Ask and answer questions about key details in a text. **Literature 3.** Describe characters, settings, and major events in a story, using key details.

Next

2. Part A

How does Little Chick's plan work?

- ○ **A.** She takes food from Dog.
- ○ **B.** She tricks Dog.
- ○ **C.** She ignores Dog.
- ○ **D.** She laughs at Dog.

Part B

Which detail from the story helps you understand how Little Chick's plan works?

- ○ **A.** Little Chick peeped, "*I* want to try."
- ○ **B.** Little Chick ran, *tippy-toe, tippy-toe,* without stopping to rest till she felt Dog's breath.
- ○ **C.** Little Chick called, "It's time to eat!"
- ○ **D.** Dog's rope was wrapped all around the tree.

Copyright © Pearson Education, Inc., or its affiliates. All Rights Reserved.

COMMON CORE STATE STANDARDS

Literature 1. Ask and answer questions about key details in a text. **Literature 3.** Describe characters, settings, and major events in a story, using key details.

Next

Name _____

Vocabulary

Directions: Read the questions below and choose the best answer.

3. **Part A**

What group does the word "growling" belong to in the following sentence?

"A big, grumpy dog came running their way, barking and growling at the end of a rope."

○ **A.** words for sounds

○ **B.** words for animals

○ **C.** words for actions

○ **D.** words for sizes

Part B

Which word in the following sentence most helps you understand the meaning of "growling"?

"A big, grumpy dog came running their way, barking and growling at the end of a rope."

○ **A.** big

○ **B.** running

○ **C.** dog

○ **D.** barking

Copyright © Pearson Education, Inc., or its affiliates. All Rights Reserved.

COMMON CORE STATE STANDARDS

Language 4. Determine or clarify the meaning of unknown and multiple-meaning words and phrases based on *grade 1 reading and content,* choosing flexibly from an array of strategies. **Language 4.a.** Use sentence-level context as a clue to the meaning of a word or phrase. **Language 5.a.** Sort words into categories (e.g., colors, clothing) to gain a sense of the concepts the categories represent.

Next

4. Part A

The word part "dis-" means "do the opposite of." What does the word "disagreed" mean in the following sentence?

"Dog disagreed, barking and pulling at the end of his rope."

- ○ **A.** didn't have the same opinion
- ○ **B.** made loud noises
- ○ **C.** didn't follow directions
- ○ **D.** acted unpleasant

Part B

Which detail from the passage most helps you choose the meaning of "disagreed"?

- ○ **A.** We're just going to the garden
- ○ **B.** A big, grumpy dog came running their way
- ○ **C.** barking and growling at the end of a rope
- ○ **D.** Little Chick ran, *tippy-toe, tippy-toe*

Copyright © Pearson Education, Inc., or its affiliates. All Rights Reserved.

COMMON CORE STATE STANDARDS

Language 4. Determine or clarify the meaning of unknown and multiple-meaning words and phrases based on *grade 1 reading and content*, choosing flexibly from an array of strategies. **Language 4.a.** Use sentence-level context as a clue to the meaning of a word or phrase. **Language 4.b.** Use frequently occurring affixes as a clue to the meaning of a word.

Next

Writing — Constructed Response

What is Little Chick like? Tell about Little Chick. Use examples from the story to support your ideas.

_____

- -

_____

- -

_____

- -

_____

_____

_____

- -

_____

_____

- -

_____

_____

- -

_____

Copyright © Pearson Education, Inc., or its affiliates. All Rights Reserved.

To the Teacher: Use the Writing Rubric on page T19 to assess children's writing.

COMMON CORE STATE STANDARDS

Literature 1. Ask and answer questions about key details in a text. **Writing 2.** Write informative/explanatory texts in which they name a topic, supply some facts about the topic, and provide some sense of closure. **Writing 8.** With guidance and support from adults, recall information from experiences or gather information from provided sources to answer a question.

Next

Writing — Extended Response

You have read two stories about characters who find clever ways to solve problems.

- *Tippy-Toe Chick, GO!*
- "Little Red Hen"

Which character do you think was most clever? Why? Write your opinion. Use details from *Tippy-Toe Chick, GO!* and "Little Red Hen" as examples in your writing. Check your writing for correct capitalization, punctuation, and spelling.

Copyright © Pearson Education, Inc., or its affiliates. All Rights Reserved.

To the Teacher: Tell children they may use the space on this page to plan their writing. Then have them write their response on the following pages. Use the Writing Rubric on page T20 to assess children's writing.

COMMON CORE STATE STANDARDS

Literature 1. Ask and answer questions about key details in a text. **Literature 3.** Describe characters, settings, and major events in a story, using key details. **Writing 1.** Write opinion pieces in which they introduce the topic or name the book they are writing about, state an opinion, supply a reason for the opinion, and provide some sense of closure. **Writing 8.** With guidance and support from adults, recall information from experiences or gather information from provided sources to answer a question. **Language 2.** Demonstrate command of the conventions of standard English capitalization, punctuation, and spelling when writing. **Language 2.a.** Capitalize dates and names of people. **Language 2.b.** Use end punctuation for sentences.

Next

Name _____

_____

- -

_____

- -

_____

- -

_____

- -

_____

- -

_____

- -

_____

- -

_____

- -

_____

- -

_____

- -

_____

- -

_____

Copyright © Pearson Education, Inc., or its affiliates. All Rights Reserved.

Next

Copyright © Pearson Education, Inc., or its affiliates. All Rights Reserved.

Name _____

Directions: Read the following passage. Use information from the passage to answer the questions.

Mole and the Baby Bird

by Marjorie Newman

Mole found a baby bird. It had fallen out of its nest. Mole waited and waited: but no big bird came to help it—so Mole took the baby bird home.

He made a nest for it. "Look!" he said to his mother.

"It's very, very hard to take care of a baby bird," she said. . . .

His friends helped him find food for the baby. His mother showed him how to feed it. Mole fed it whenever it chirped. . . .

The bird fluttered its wings. "Your bird is trying to fly," said his mother. "No!" cried Mole. "It mustn't fly!"

Mole found some wood and some nails. He borrowed his dad's toolbox. "What are you making?" asked his dad. "I'm making a cage for my pet bird!" said Mole.

"It's not a pet bird. It's a wild bird," said his dad. "You should let it fly." "No!" cried Mole.

Copyright © Pearson Education, Inc., or its affiliates. All Rights Reserved.

Next

He put his bird into its new cage. The bird was sad. Mole's mother was sad too. But Mole kept his bird, because he loved it.

Then—Grandad came to visit. He looked at Mole's pet bird. Presently Grandad said, "Let's go for a walk, little Mole."

Grandad took Mole to the top of a high hill.

Mole looked down at the trees far below.

He felt the wild wind trying to lift him. "Wheee! I'm flying!" cried Mole. "Nearly," said Grandad.

When Mole got home he looked at his bird. It was sitting very still in its cage in Mole's dark underground room. "Birds are meant to fly," said Mole.

He opened the cage door, and he let his bird fly away because he loved it. Then he cried.

The next day Mole went into the forest. He saw his bird flying, soaring, free. And Mole was glad.

Copyright © Pearson Education, Inc., or its affiliates. All Rights Reserved.

Next

Name _____

Text-Based Comprehension

Directions: Read the questions below and choose the best answer.

1. Part A

Why does Mole make a cage for his bird?

○ **A.** So the bird will be happy.

○ **B.** So he can feed the bird better.

○ **C.** So his dad will be proud of him.

○ **D.** So he can keep the bird nearby.

Part B

Which sentence from the story best helps you answer why Mole makes a cage?

○ **A.** His mother showed him how to feed it.

○ **B.** He borrowed his dad's toolbox.

○ **C.** "It mustn't fly!"

○ **D.** His friends helped him find food for the baby.

Copyright © Pearson Education, Inc., or its affiliates. All Rights Reserved.

COMMON CORE STATE STANDARDS

Literature 1. Ask and answer questions about key details in a text. **Literature 3.** Describe characters, settings, and major events in a story, using key details.

Next

2. Part A

How does Grandad help Mole?

○ **A.** He shows Mole what flying is like.

○ **B.** He helps Mole get exercise.

○ **C.** He has a special day with Mole.

○ **D.** He shows Mole how to climb a hill.

Part B

Which detail from the story helps you understand how Grandad helped Mole?

○ **A.** "Let's go for a walk, little Mole."

○ **B.** Grandad took Mole to the top of a high hill.

○ **C.** Mole looked down at the trees far below.

○ **D.** "Wheee! I'm flying!" cried Mole.

Copyright © Pearson Education, Inc., or its affiliates. All Rights Reserved.

COMMON CORE STATE STANDARDS

Literature 1. Ask and answer questions about key details in a text. **Literature 3.** Describe characters, settings, and major events in a story, using key details.

Next

Vocabulary

Directions: Read the questions below and choose the best answer.

3. Part A

Which sentence contains a compound word, a word made of two separate words?

- ○ **A.** Mole found some wood and some nails.
- ○ **B.** He borrowed his dad's toolbox.
- ○ **C.** The bird fluttered its wings.
- ○ **D.** He felt the wild wind trying to lift him.

Part B

Which of the following sentences most helps you figure out the meaning of the compound word you found?

- ○ **A.** "What are you making?" asked his dad.
- ○ **B.** "Your bird is trying to fly," said his mother.
- ○ **C.** "Wheee! I'm flying!" cried Mole.
- ○ **D.** When Mole got home he looked at his bird.

Copyright © Pearson Education, Inc., or its affiliates. All Rights Reserved.

COMMON CORE STATE STANDARDS

Language 4. Determine or clarify the meaning of unknown and multiple-meaning words and phrases based on *grade 1 reading and content,* choosing flexibly from an array of strategies. **Language 4.a.** Use sentence-level context as a clue to the meaning of a word or phrase.

Next

4. Part A

What does the word "wild" mean in the following sentence?

"He felt the wild wind trying to lift him."

○ **A.** strong

○ **B.** gentle

○ **C.** underground

○ **D.** like an animal

Part B

Which sentence in the passage helps you understand the meaning of "wild"?

○ **A.** Mole looked down at the trees far below.

○ **B.** Then he cried.

○ **C.** And Mole was glad.

○ **D.** "Wheee! I'm flying!" cried Mole.

Copyright © Pearson Education, Inc., or its affiliates. All Rights Reserved.

COMMON CORE STATE STANDARDS

Language 4. Determine or clarify the meaning of unknown and multiple-meaning words and phrases based on *grade 1 reading and content,* choosing flexibly from an array of strategies. **Language 4.a.** Use sentence-level context as a clue to the meaning of a word or phrase.

Next

Writing — Constructed Response

What kind of pet would you like? Where would you keep your pet? How would your pet be different from Mole's pet? Use details from the story to help you answer the questions.

_____

- -

_____

_____

- -

_____

_____

- -

_____

_____

- -

_____

_____

- -

_____

Copyright © Pearson Education, Inc., or its affiliates. All Rights Reserved.

To the Teacher: Use the Writing Rubric on page T19 to assess children's writing.

COMMON CORE STATE STANDARDS

Literature 1. Ask and answer questions about key details in a text. **Writing 2.** Write informative/explanatory texts in which they name a topic, supply some facts about the topic, and provide some sense of closure. **Writing 8.** With guidance and support from adults, recall information from experiences or gather information from provided sources to answer a question.

Next

Writing — Extended Response

You have read two stories about characters who do hard things.

- *Mole and the Baby Bird*
- "Brave Little Cuckoo"

Think about a hard thing you did. How did you feel after you did it? What did you learn? Use details from *Mole and Baby Bird* and "Brave Little Cuckoo" as examples in your writing. Check your writing for correct capitalization, punctuation, and spelling.

Copyright © Pearson Education, Inc., or its affiliates. All Rights Reserved.

To the Teacher: Tell children they may use the space on this page to plan their writing. Then have them write their response on the following pages. Use the Writing Rubric on page T20 to assess children's writing.

COMMON CORE STATE STANDARDS

Literature 1. Ask and answer questions about key details in a text. **Writing 2.** Write informative/explanatory texts in which they name a topic, supply some facts about the topic, and provide some sense of closure. **Writing 8.** With guidance and support from adults, recall information from experiences or gather information from provided sources to answer a question. **Language 2.** Demonstrate command of the conventions of standard English capitalization, punctuation, and spelling when writing. **Language 2.a.** Capitalize dates and names of people. **Language 2.b.** Use end punctuation for sentences.

Next

Name _____

Copyright © Pearson Education, Inc., or its affiliates. All Rights Reserved.

Copyright © Pearson Education, Inc., or its affiliates. All Rights Reserved.

Name _____

Directions: Read the following passage. Use information from the passage to answer the questions.

Dot & Jabber and the Great Acorn Mystery

by Ellen Stoll Walsh

The detectives had nothing to do. "We need a mystery to solve," said Jabber. "Here's a mystery," said Dot. "What is this little oak tree doing here?"

"Why is that a mystery?" Jabber wanted to know. "Because of the acorn," said Dot. "How did it get here?" "Dot," said Jabber, "what acorn?"

"Acorns are oak tree seeds. This little oak tree grew from an acorn, and acorns come from big oak trees." "Oh, *that* acorn," said Jabber. "But where's the big oak tree?"

"That's part of the mystery," said Dot. "Let's look for clues." "Okay!" shouted Jabber. "Because we're detectives!" He poked his head into a hole.

"Hey, this is *my* hole," said a mole. "Go away. There are no clues down here. Try the big oak tree—on the *other* side of the meadow." . . .

At last they arrived at the big oak tree. "Look!" said Dot. "I bet there are a million acorns here."

Copyright © Pearson Education, Inc., or its affiliates. All Rights Reserved.

Next

"They don't have wings," said Jabber. "But they taste good." "Don't eat them, Jabber! They're clues."

"Acorns don't have wings, but they might have sneaky feet," said Dot. "Let's keep watch and see if they start to move." . . .

A squirrel came and sat down among the acorns. "Jabber, look!" Dot whispered. "What is he doing?" "Oh!" gasped Jabber. "He's eating our clue!" "He can't be," said Dot. "The shell is still on it."

"So why is he stuffing it in his mouth?" asked Jabber. The squirrel ran off. "Oh no, he's stealing the acorn!" the detectives cried and ran after him.

When the squirrel stopped, they stopped and watched to see what would happen next. "What's he doing now?" asked Jabber. "Digging a hole. Look! He's hiding the acorn." Jabber stared at Dot. "Maybe he's planting it!"

"Of course!" said Dot. "Our acorn crossed the meadow on squirrel feet." "And got planted by squirrel feet," said Jabber. "And grew into the little oak tree," said Dot. "The mystery is solved. We are two clever mouse detectives!"

"Hurray!" shouted Jabber. "Now what will we do?" "Find another mystery," said Dot. "But I'm hungry," said Jabber. "First let's go eat some of those leftover clues."

Copyright © Pearson Education, Inc., or its affiliates. All Rights Reserved.

Next

Name _____

Text-Based Comprehension

Directions: Read the questions below and choose the best answer.

I. Part A

Which word best describes how Dot and Jabber are alike?

○ **A.** curious

○ **B.** helpful

○ **C.** bashful

○ **D.** tricky

Part B

Which detail from the story best shows you how Dot and Jabber are alike?

○ **A.** "First let's go eat some of those leftover clues."

○ **B.** "Don't eat them, Jabber! They're clues."

○ **C.** "What is this little oak tree doing here?"

○ **D.** "We are two clever mouse detectives!"

Copyright © Pearson Education, Inc., or its affiliates. All Rights Reserved.

COMMON CORE STATE STANDARDS

Literature 1. Ask and answer questions about key details in a text. **Literature 3.** Describe characters, settings, and major events in a story, using key details. **Literature 9.** Compare and contrast the adventures and experiences of characters in stories.

Next

2. Part A

What mystery do Dot and Jabber solve?

○ **A.** how acorns get far away from oak trees

○ **B.** what happened to a big oak tree

○ **C.** why squirrels eat acorns

○ **D.** how many acorns are under an oak tree

Part B

Which sentence from the story helps you know what mystery Dot and Jabber solve?

○ **A.** "But where's the big oak tree?"

○ **B.** "I bet there are a million acorns here."

○ **C.** "Our acorn crossed the meadow on squirrel feet."

○ **D.** "So why is he stuffing it in his mouth?" asked Jabber.

Copyright © Pearson Education, Inc., or its affiliates. All Rights Reserved.

COMMON CORE STATE STANDARDS

Literature 1. Ask and answer questions about key details in a text. **Literature 3.** Describe characters, settings, and major events in a story, using key details.

Next

Vocabulary

Directions: Read the questions below and choose the best answer.

3. Part A

What is the meaning of the word "detective" in the selection?

- ○ **A.** a person who asks questions
- ○ **B.** a person who solves mysteries
- ○ **C.** someone who finds people who steal
- ○ **D.** someone who studies nature

Part B

Which sentence gives the best clue to the meaning of "detective"?

- ○ **A.** "We need a mystery to solve," said Jabber.
- ○ **B.** "Oh no, he's stealing the acorn!"
- ○ **C.** "Because we're detectives!"
- ○ **D.** At last they arrived at the big oak tree.

Copyright © Pearson Education, Inc., or its affiliates. All Rights Reserved.

COMMON CORE STATE STANDARDS

Language 4. Determine or clarify the meaning of unknown and multiple-meaning words and phrases based on *grade 1 reading and content,* choosing flexibly from an array of strategies. **Language 4.a.** Use sentence-level context as a clue to the meaning of a word or phrase.

Next

4. Part A

Which sentence contains a compound word, a word made from two separate words?

○ **A.** "We need a mystery to solve," said Jabber.

○ **B.** At last they arrived at the big oak tree.

○ **C.** "Acorns don't have wings, but they might have sneaky feet," said Dot.

○ **D.** "First let's go eat some of those leftover clues."

Part B

Which sentence helps you understand the meaning of the compound word?

○ **A.** "They don't have wings," said Jabber.

○ **B.** "I bet there are a million acorns here."

○ **C.** "Our acorn crossed the meadow on squirrel feet."

○ **D.** "What is this little oak tree doing here?"

Copyright © Pearson Education, Inc., or its affiliates. All Rights Reserved.

COMMON CORE STATE STANDARDS

Language 4. Determine or clarify the meaning of unknown and multiple-meaning words and phrases based on *grade 1 reading and content*, choosing flexibly from an array of strategies. **Language 4.a.** Use sentence-level context as a clue to the meaning of a word or phrase.

Next

Name _____

Writing — Constructed Response

Dot and Jabber solve a nature mystery. What mystery about nature have you solved? Tell about something you have wondered about. Then tell the answer to the mystery. Use examples from the story.

_____

_____

_____

_____

_____

_____

_____

_____

_____

_____

_____

Copyright © Pearson Education, Inc., or its affiliates. All Rights Reserved.

To the Teacher: Use the Writing Rubric on page T19 to assess children's writing.

COMMON CORE STATE STANDARDS

Literature 1. Ask and answer questions about key details in a text. **Writing 2.** Write informative/explanatory texts in which they name a topic, supply some facts about the topic, and provide some sense of closure. **Writing 8.** With guidance and support from adults, recall information from experiences or gather information from provided sources to answer a question.

Next

Writing — Extended Response

You have read two stories about how things happen in nature.

- *Dot & Jabber and the Great Acorn Mystery*
- "Water"

Think about an animal or plant you like. Tell how you could find out more about the plant or animal. Use details from *Dot & Jabber and the Great Acorn Mystery* and "Water" as a model for your writing. Check your writing for correct capitalization, punctuation, and spelling.

Copyright © Pearson Education, Inc., or its affiliates. All Rights Reserved.

To the Teacher: Tell children they may use the space on this page to plan their writing. Then have them write their response on the following pages. Use the Writing Rubric on page T20 to assess children's writing.

COMMON CORE STATE STANDARDS

Literature 1. Ask and answer questions about key details in a text. **Writing 2.** Write informative/explanatory texts in which they name a topic, supply some facts about the topic, and provide some sense of closure. **Writing 8.** With guidance and support from adults, recall information from experiences or gather information from provided sources to answer a question. **Language 2.** Demonstrate command of the conventions of standard English capitalization, punctuation, and spelling when writing. **Language 2.b.** Use end punctuation for sentences. **Language 2.d.** Use conventional spelling for words with common spelling patterns and for frequently occurring irregular words.

Next

Name _____

_____

- -

_____

_____

- -

_____

_____

- -

_____

_____

- -

_____

_____

- -

_____

_____

- -

_____

_____

- -

_____

_____

- -

_____

Copyright © Pearson Education, Inc., or its affiliates. All Rights Reserved.

Next

Copyright © Pearson Education, Inc., or its affiliates. All Rights Reserved.

Name _____

Directions: Read the following passage. Use information from the
passage to answer the questions.

Simple Machines

by Allan Fowler

We use machines every day. Machines help make our
lives easier. Some machines, such as lawn mowers and
vacuum cleaners, have many parts.

Other machines have few parts. They are called
simple machines. Levers, inclined planes, wheels and
axles, and pulleys are four kinds of simple machines.

[A] bottle opener is a kind of lever. It helps you remove
the cap from a bottle.

Some levers can help you move a heavy object, such
as a rock. Push down on one end of a lever. The other
end moves up and pushes against whatever you are
trying to move.

Have you ever ridden a seesaw?

A seesaw is a kind of lever. One side goes up, while
the other side goes down.

Inclined planes are all around you.

A plane is just a flat surface, like a wooden board. An
inclined plane is a flat surface that is slanted.

Copyright © Pearson Education, Inc., or its affiliates. All Rights Reserved.

Next

Ramps are inclined planes. It is easier to push a big load up a ramp than to lift it.

A wedge is another kind of inclined plane. A wedge can help you cut wood. When a wedge is hit with a big hammer, its thin part splits the wood.

Wheels help things go. An axle, or rod, connects a pair of wheels. The axle helps the wheels turn.

Wheels are on bicycles and cars. It would be very hard to move a bike or car without wheels.

A pulley helps you lift heavy objects. A pulley's rope passes over a small wheel. Pull down on one end of the rope. You can lift a very heavy load tied to the other end.

A pulley can help you raise and lower the flag on a flagpole. You can even lift the sail on a boat using a pulley. . . .

Have you used any simple machines today?

Copyright © Pearson Education, Inc., or its affiliates. All Rights Reserved.

Next

Name _____

Text-Based Comprehension

Directions: Read the questions below and choose the best answer.

I. Part A

How are levers and pulleys alike?

○ **A.** They can both help lift heavy things.

○ **B.** They both have wheels.

○ **C.** They are both inclined planes.

○ **D.** They can both help cut things.

Part B

Which sentence from the selection helps you understand how a lever or a pulley works?

○ **A.** An inclined plane is a flat surface that is slanted.

○ **B.** It is easier to push a big load up a ramp than to lift it.

○ **C.** Some levers can help you move a heavy object, such as a rock.

○ **D.** A wedge is another kind of inclined plane.

Copyright © Pearson Education, Inc., or its affiliates. All Rights Reserved.

COMMON CORE STATE STANDARDS

Informational Text 1. Ask and answer questions about key details in a text. **Informational Text 3.** Describe the connection between two individuals, events, ideas, or pieces of information in a text.

Next

2. Part A

Which is an unstated main idea of the selection?

○ **A.** People don't use simple machines to do work.

○ **B.** Grown-ups don't use simple machines.

○ **C.** Wheels are the most useful simple machines.

○ **D.** Simple machines don't need motors to work.

Part B

Which sentence from the selection provides supporting details for the main idea?

○ **A.** Machines help make our lives easier.

○ **B.** An inclined plane is a flat surface that is slanted.

○ **C.** Other machines have few parts.

○ **D.** Some machines, such as lawn mowers and vacuum cleaners, have many parts.

Copyright © Pearson Education, Inc., or its affiliates. All Rights Reserved.

COMMON CORE STATE STANDARDS

Informational Text 1. Ask and answer questions about key details in a text. **Informational Text 2.** Identify the main topic and retell key details of a text.

Next

Name _____

Vocabulary

Directions: Read the questions below and choose the best answer.

3. Part A

What is the best meaning of "machine" in the passage?

○ **A.** something that helps people move

○ **B.** anything people use every day

○ **C.** a thing that helps people do work

○ **D.** a tool with many parts

Part B

Which sentence most helps you understand the meaning of "machine" in the passage?

○ **A.** We use machines every day.

○ **B.** Machines help make our lives easier.

○ **C.** Some machines, such as lawn mowers and vacuum cleaners, have many parts.

○ **D.** It would be very hard to move a bike or car without wheels.

Copyright © Pearson Education, Inc., or its affiliates. All Rights Reserved.

COMMON CORE STATE STANDARDS

Language 4. Determine or clarify the meaning of unknown and multiple-meaning words and phrases based on *grade 1 reading and content,* choosing flexibly from an array of strategies. **Language 4.a.** Use sentence-level context as a clue to the meaning of a word or phrase.

Next

4. Part A

What does an "axle" look like?

"An axle, or rod, connects a pair of wheels."

- ○ **A.** long and narrow
- ○ **B.** soft and stretchy
- ○ **C.** two-sided
- ○ **D.** sharp and pointed

Part B

Which word in the sentence most helps you understand what an "axle" is like?

- ○ **A.** rod
- ○ **B.** connects
- ○ **C.** pair
- ○ **D.** wheels

Copyright © Pearson Education, Inc., or its affiliates. All Rights Reserved.

COMMON CORE STATE STANDARDS

Language 4. Determine or clarify the meaning of unknown and multiple-meaning words and phrases based on *grade 1 reading and content,* choosing flexibly from an array of strategies. **Language 4.a.** Use sentence-level context as a clue to the meaning of a word or phrase.

Next

Writing — Constructed Response

What simple machine do you use every day? Describe how you use it. Use details from the passage to help you write.

_____
- -
_____
- -
_____
- -
_____
- -
_____
- -
_____
- -
_____
- -
_____
- -

Copyright © Pearson Education, Inc., or its affiliates. All Rights Reserved.

To the Teacher: Use the Writing Rubric on page T19 to assess children's writing.

COMMON CORE STATE STANDARDS

Informational Text 1. Ask and answer questions about key details in a text. **Writing 2.** Write informative/ explanatory texts in which they name a topic, supply some facts about the topic, and provide some sense of closure. **Writing 8.** With guidance and support from adults, recall information from experiences or gather information from provided sources to answer a question.

Next

Writing — Extended Response

You have read two selections about machines.

- *Simple Machines*
- "Roy's Wheelchair"

A wheelchair is a machine made from a simple machine, the wheel. Describe another invention made from a simple machine. Explain how the invention helps people. Check your writing for correct capitalization, punctuation, and spelling.

To the Teacher: Tell children they may use the space on this page to plan their writing. Then have them write their response on the following pages. Use the Writing Rubric on page T20 to assess children's writing.

Copyright © Pearson Education, Inc., or its affiliates. All Rights Reserved.

COMMON CORE STATE STANDARDS

Informational Text 1. Ask and answer questions about key details in a text. **Writing 2.** Write informative/explanatory texts in which they name a topic, supply some facts about the topic, and provide some sense of closure. **Writing 8.** With guidance and support from adults, recall information from experiences or gather information from provided sources to answer a question. **Language 2.** Demonstrate command of the conventions of standard English capitalization, punctuation, and spelling when writing. **Language 2.b.** Use end punctuation for sentences. **Language 2.d.** Use conventional spelling for words with common spelling patterns and for frequently occurring irregular words.

Next

Name _____

Copyright © Pearson Education, Inc., or its affiliates. All Rights Reserved.

Copyright © Pearson Education, Inc., or its affiliates. All Rights Reserved.

Name _____

Directions: Read the following passage. Use information from the passage to answer the questions.

Alexander Graham Bell: A Great Inventor

by Lynne Blanton

Early Life

Alexander Graham Bell was born in Scotland in 1847. His family called him Aleck for short. His mom was deaf. His dad helped deaf boys and girls learn how to speak.

Aleck liked playing music. His mom taught him how to play the piano at an early age. She could not hear, but that did not stop her. . . .

As a teen, Aleck liked studying the science of sound. But what he liked best was inventing new things. He daydreamed about things he could make. . . .

New Home

When he was twenty-three, Aleck Bell got awfully sick. He left his boyhood home. He and his family went to Canada. They hoped he would get well in this new place, and he did.

Then Bell went to Boston in the United States. He taught speech for deaf students like his dad did.

Copyright © Pearson Education, Inc., or its affiliates. All Rights Reserved.

Next

Bell liked teaching, but he liked inventing things better. He started spending less time teaching and more time inventing.

Great Idea

One day, while shopping for supplies, Bell met Thomas Watson. Watson, a skillful toolmaker, had helped many inventors before he met Bell. Bell told Watson about his latest plan for a telephone.

Bell and Watson worked long days and nights on Bell's plan. Bell started thinking his plan might succeed. He got a patent for the first telephone. A patent says an inventor owns and can make and sell the thing he or she invents.

The first telephone call took place on March 10, 1876.

That day, Bell dropped a jar by mistake. It spilled and he called for help.

"Mr. Watson, come here. I want you!" he called.

At least, that's how the story goes.

Watson came running. He had heard Bell's voice through the wires! The phone worked! . . .

Bell kept on inventing things until his death in 1922. He will always keep his place as one of the greatest inventors of all time.

Copyright © Pearson Education, Inc., or its affiliates. All Rights Reserved.

Next

Name _____

Text-Based Comprehension

Directions: Read the questions below and choose the best answer.

I. Part A

What was Aleck's favorite thing to do when he was young?

○ **A.** daydream

○ **B.** study sound

○ **C.** teach deaf students

○ **D.** invent new things

Part B

Where should you look to find the answer to Aleck's favorite thing to do?

○ **A.** under the subheading "Early Life"

○ **B.** under the subheading "New Home"

○ **C.** under the subheading "Great Idea"

○ **D.** through the whole passage

Copyright © Pearson Education, Inc., or its affiliates. All Rights Reserved.

COMMON CORE STATE STANDARDS

Informational Text 1. Ask and answer questions about key details in a text. **Informational Text 5.** Know and use various text features (e.g., headings, tables of contents, glossaries, electronic menus, icons) to locate key facts or information in a text.

Next

2. Part A

What did Bell do next after he and his family moved to Canada?

○ **A.** He got sick.

○ **B.** He moved to Boston.

○ **C.** He met Thomas Watson.

○ **D.** He invented the telephone.

Part B

Which word in the passage helps you know what happened next after Bell and his family moved to Canada?

○ **A.** when

○ **B.** and

○ **C.** then

○ **D.** but

Copyright © Pearson Education, Inc., or its affiliates. All Rights Reserved.

COMMON CORE STATE STANDARDS

Informational Text 1. Ask and answer questions about key details in a text.

Next

Name _____

Vocabulary

Directions: Read the questions below and choose the best answer.

3. **Part A**

Which sentence from the selection contains a compound word, a word made from two separate words?

○ **A.** He daydreamed about things he could make.

○ **B.** Then Bell went to Boston in the United States.

○ **C.** His dad helped deaf boys and girls learn how to speak.

○ **D.** But what he liked best was inventing new things.

Part B

Which other sentence from the selection contains a compound word?

○ **A.** One day, while shopping for supplies, Bell met Thomas Watson.

○ **B.** Watson, a skillful toolmaker, had helped many inventors before he met Bell.

○ **C.** Bell told Watson about his latest plan for a telephone.

○ **D.** Bell and Watson worked long days and nights on Bell's plan.

Copyright © Pearson Education, Inc., or its affiliates. All Rights Reserved.

COMMON CORE STATE STANDARDS

Language 4. Determine or clarify the meaning of unknown and multiple-meaning words and phrases based on *grade 1 reading and content,* choosing flexibly from an array of strategies. **Language 4.a.** Use sentence-level context as a clue to the meaning of a word or phrase.

Next

4. Part A

What does the phrase "through the wires" mean in the following sentence?

"He had heard Bell's voice through the wires!"

○ **A.** around the room

○ **B.** through glass

○ **C.** because of electric lights

○ **D.** over the telephone

Part B

Which sentence most helps the reader understand the meaning of "through the wires" in the sentence?

○ **A.** That day, Bell dropped a jar by mistake.

○ **B.** Watson came running.

○ **C.** The phone worked!

○ **D.** Bell kept on inventing things until his death in 1922.

Copyright © Pearson Education, Inc., or its affiliates. All Rights Reserved.

COMMON CORE STATE STANDARDS

Informational Text 4. Ask and answer questions to help determine or clarify the meaning of words and phrases in a text. **Language 4.** Determine or clarify the meaning of unknown and multiple-meaning words and phrases based on *grade 1 reading and content,* choosing flexibly from an array of strategies. **Language 4.a.** Use sentence-level context as a clue to the meaning of a word or phrase.

Next

Name _____

Writing – Constructed Response

Why was the telephone an important invention? Use details from the passage to help you answer the question.

_____

_____

_____

_____

_____

_____

_____

_____

_____

_____

Copyright © Pearson Education, Inc., or its affiliates. All Rights Reserved.

To the Teacher: Use the Writing Rubric on page T19 to assess children's writing.

COMMON CORE STATE STANDARDS

Informational Text 1. Ask and answer questions about key details in a text. **Writing 2.** Write informative/explanatory texts in which they name a topic, supply some facts about the topic, and provide some sense of closure. **Writing 8.** With guidance and support from adults, recall information from experiences or gather information from provided sources to answer a question.

Next

Writing — Extended Response

You have read two selections about inventions.

- *Alexander Graham Bell: A Great Inventor*
- "Inventions"

What invention do you think was the most important? How did it change people's lives? Use details from *Alexander Graham Bell: A Great Inventor* and "Inventions" to help you answer the questions. Check your writing for correct capitalization, punctuation, and spelling.

Copyright © Pearson Education, Inc., or its affiliates. All Rights Reserved.

To the Teacher: Tell children they may use the space on this page to plan their writing. Then have them write their response on the following pages. Use the Writing Rubric on page T20 to assess children's writing.

COMMON CORE STATE STANDARDS

Informational Text 1. Ask and answer questions about key details in a text. **Writing 1.** Write opinion pieces in which they introduce the topic or name the book they are writing about, state an opinion, supply a reason for the opinion, and provide some sense of closure. **Writing 8.** With guidance and support from adults, recall information from experiences or gather information from provided sources to answer a question. **Language 2.** Demonstrate command of the conventions of standard English capitalization, punctuation, and spelling when writing. **Language 2.a.** Capitalize dates and names of people. **Language 2.b.** Use end punctuation for sentences.

Next

Name _____

Copyright © Pearson Education, Inc., or its affiliates. All Rights Reserved.

Copyright © Pearson Education, Inc., or its affiliates. All Rights Reserved.

Name _____

Directions: Read the following passage. Use information from the passage to answer the questions.

Common Language
by Helen Pettigrew

My new friend spoke to me in French,
And I couldn't tell what she said.
When I tried to answer her,
She only shook her head.
Suddenly both of us laughed,
And it was then we found
The wonderful language of laughter
Is known the wide world round!

Copyright © Pearson Education, Inc., or its affiliates. All Rights Reserved.

Next

A Map and a Dream

by Karen O'Donnell Taylor

Maps are more
than tiny lines
intersecting
lace designs . . .
More than names
and colored dots,
rivers, mountains,
tourist spots.
Maps are keys
to secret places
vast new worlds
and unknown faces.
I can trace each
graceful line . . .

Close my eyes
and in my mind
I can travel
anywhere . . .
A map, a dream
can take me there!

Copyright © Pearson Education, Inc., or its affiliates. All Rights Reserved.

Next

Text-Based Comprehension

Directions: Read the questions below and choose the best answer.

1. Part A

What is the speaker's main idea in "A Map and a Dream"?

○ **A.** Maps are interesting.

○ **B.** Maps are beautiful.

○ **C.** Maps make her daydream.

○ **D.** Maps help her find her way.

Part B

Which words from the poem help you know the main idea?

○ **A.** intersecting lace designs

○ **B.** rivers, mountains, tourist spots

○ **C.** I can trace each graceful line

○ **D.** in my mind I can travel anywhere

Copyright © Pearson Education, Inc., or its affiliates. All Rights Reserved.

COMMON CORE STATE STANDARDS

Literature 1. Ask and answer questions about key details in a text.

Next

2. Part A

How are the themes of the two poems alike?

○ **A.** They are both about maps.

○ **B.** They are both about people from other countries.

○ **C.** They are both about laughing.

○ **D.** They are both about faraway places.

Part B

Which details from the poems help you know how the themes are alike?

○ **A.** the wide world round; vast new worlds and unknown faces

○ **B.** The wonderful language of laughter; More than names and colored dots

○ **C.** Maps are keys to secret places; Suddenly both of us laughed,

○ **D.** rivers, mountains, tourist spots; I couldn't tell what she said

Copyright © Pearson Education, Inc., or its affiliates. All Rights Reserved.

COMMON CORE STATE STANDARDS

Literature 1. Ask and answer questions about key details in a text. **Literature 2.** Retell stories, including key details, and demonstrate understanding of their central message or lesson.

Next

Name _____

Vocabulary

Directions: Read the questions below and choose the best answer.

3. Part A

In the poem "Common Language," what does the speaker mean by the "language of laughter"?

- ○ **A.** People laugh in different ways.
- ○ **B.** Everyone likes to laugh together.
- ○ **C.** People who speak French laugh a lot.
- ○ **D.** Instead of talking, just laugh.

Part B

Which words from the poem best help you know what the speaker means?

- ○ **A.** My new friend spoke to me in French
- ○ **B.** I couldn't tell what she said
- ○ **C.** She only shook her head
- ○ **D.** Suddenly both of us laughed

Copyright © Pearson Education, Inc., or its affiliates. All Rights Reserved.

COMMON CORE STATE STANDARDS

Language 4. Determine or clarify the meaning of unknown and multiple-meaning words and phrases based on *grade 1 reading and content,* choosing flexibly from an array of strategies. **Language 4.a.** Use sentence-level context as a clue to the meaning of a word or phrase.

Next

4. Part A

What do the words "lace designs" mean in the poem
"A Map and a Dream"?

○ **A.** The map is made of cloth.

○ **B.** The map marks look like lace.

○ **C.** The map is stitched together.

○ **D.** The map has holes in it.

Part B

Which words from the poem help you know what the words
"lace designs" mean?

○ **A.** More than names and colored dots

○ **B.** I can trace each graceful line

○ **C.** Close my eyes

○ **D.** keys to secret places

Copyright © Pearson Education, Inc., or its affiliates. All Rights Reserved.

COMMON CORE STATE STANDARDS

Language 4. Determine or clarify the meaning of unknown and multiple-meaning words and phrases based on *grade 1 reading and content,* choosing flexibly from an array of strategies. **Language 4.a.** Use sentence-level context as a clue to the meaning of a word or phrase.

Next

Name _____

Writing — Constructed Response

What place in the world would you like to go? What would you say and do with a new friend there? Use ideas from "Common Language" and "A Map and a Dream" to help you write.

_____

_____

_____

_____

_____

_____

_____

_____

_____

Copyright © Pearson Education, Inc., or its affiliates. All Rights Reserved.

To the Teacher: Use the Writing Rubric on page T19 to assess children's writing.

COMMON CORE STATE STANDARDS

Literature 1. Ask and answer questions about key details in a text. **Writing 2.** Write informative/explanatory texts in which they name a topic, supply some facts about the topic, and provide some sense of closure. **Writing 8.** With guidance and support from adults, recall information from experiences or gather information from provided sources to answer a question.

Next

Writing — Extended Response

You have read two selections about using your imagination.

- *The Stone Garden*
- "Common Language" and "A Map and a Dream"

How have you used your imagination to do something special? Tell what you imagined. Use details from *The Stone Garden* and the poems as examples in your writing. Check your writing for correct capitalization, punctuation, and spelling.

Copyright © Pearson Education, Inc., or its affiliates. All Rights Reserved.

To the Teacher: Tell children they may use the space on this page to plan their writing. Then have them write their response on the following pages. Use the Writing Rubric on page T20 to assess children's writing.

COMMON CORE STATE STANDARDS

Literature 1. Ask and answer questions about key details in a text. **Writing 3.** Write narratives in which they recount two or more appropriately sequenced events, include some details regarding what happened, use temporal words to signal event order, and provide some sense of closure. **Language 2.** Demonstrate command of the conventions of standard English capitalization, punctuation, and spelling when writing. **Language 2.b.** Use end punctuation for sentences. **Language 2.d.** Use conventional spelling for words with common spelling patterns and for frequently occurring irregular words.

Next

Name _____

Copyright © Pearson Education, Inc., or its affiliates. All Rights Reserved.

_____

- -

_____

- -

_____

- -

_____

- -

_____

- -

_____

- -

_____

- -

_____

- -

_____

- -

_____

- -

_____

Copyright © Pearson Education, Inc., or its affiliates. All Rights Reserved.